RHYTHM OF LOVE

"Carl, I had a wonderful time today," Darcy said softly, standing just inches away from him. She lifted her face to his. *Do I love Carl?* she wondered. The thought shook her so much she couldn't meet his eyes. If she loved Carl, then how did she feel about Scott? And if she loved Scott, how did she really feel about Carl? You couldn't love two people at the same time—or could you?

Rhythm Of Love

Stephanie Foster

BANTAM BOOKS
TORONTO · NEW YORK · LONDON · SYDNEY

RL 5, IL age 11 and up

RHYTHM OF LOVE
A Bantam Book / April 1984
Reprinted 1985

Cover photo by Pat Hill

ISBN 0-553-17872-5

Published simultaneously in the United States and Canada

Bantam Books are published by Bantam Books, Inc. Its trademark, consisting of the words "Bantam Books" and the portrayal of a rooster, is registered in U.S. Patent and Trademark Office and in other countries. Marca Registrada. Bantam Books, Inc., 666 Fifth Avenue, New York, New York 10103.

Printed and bound in Great Britain by Hunt Barnard Printing Ltd.

O   0 9 8 7 6 5 4 3 2 1

For Amanda

Rhythm Of Love

Chapter One

"Hey, Darcy! Wait up!"

Darcy Bennett had been hurrying down the crowded corridor of Kennedy High, but she stopped suddenly and clutched her books to her chest. A little tingle ran down her spine at the sound of that familiar voice, and she turned her head to see Scott Maguire, tall, dark, and gorgeous, coming toward her. As usual, he was surrounded by a crowd, many of whom Darcy recognized as Jupiter groupies, girls who came to every dance Scott's rock group played at or every concert they gave. They would crowd up close to the stage, jumping up and down and screaming.

Darcy was Jupiter's keyboardist, the only

girl in the band. If she could be the only girl in Scott's life, she thought, she would be totally happy. She was convinced it was just a matter of time before Scott realized he cared as much for her as he did for his music—at least, she fervently hoped so.

Scott had caught up with her, grinning his lopsided smile. She felt like melting, but instead she smiled back at him radiantly.

"Practice at four o'clock, Tommy's basement, right?" she asked.

"Well, yeah, that's what I want to talk to you about," Scott replied. "Stash your stuff in your locker, and get your coat. I'll meet you out front, and we'll go to Hoagie Haven for a Coke. Five minutes, OK?"

"Sure, OK," said Darcy, puzzled but elated. Scott had never asked her out for even so much as a soda. *What did he have in mind?* she wondered as he turned abruptly and disappeared into the clamoring crowd heading for freedom after another long school day. Bemused, she went to her locker, put away the books she wouldn't need that night, and checked herself in the little mirror she had taped to the door.

Everything looked OK—dark, shoulder-length hair, smooth and shiny; wide hazel eyes, clear and sparkling; skin without a blemish—thank goodness. Nothing outstanding, but not bad. Quickly she applied some of her new lip gloss, touched a little blusher to her cheeks, and shrugged into her maroon down jacket. She picked up her books. Maybe she wasn't as glamorous as some of the girls who hung around Scott, but she was pretty enough, and she was talented musically, which should appeal to Scott. He was very serious about his music. And he'd asked *her* to go to Hoagie Haven. What more could she want? As an afterthought she drew back her lips and examined her teeth to make sure there was no leftover lunch between them. No, clean and straight as five years' orthodontia could make them.

Darcy slammed her locker door shut and twisted the dial. She was hurrying down the corridor to the main entrance when she saw her best friend, Miranda Alfano, running toward her and waving madly.

"Hey, Darcy, got a minute?" she asked breathlessly.

Miranda skidded to a stop beside Darcy, frizzy brown hair flying, blue eyes shining.

As usual, she was lugging an armload of books and papers, most of which were in imminent danger of falling. Miranda looked like a complete scatterbrain, but Darcy knew that beneath that frantic exterior was a highly intelligent, incredibly organized girl.

"Well, maybe a minute, but that's all," said Darcy, beaming. "I'm meeting Scott outside."

"How come so early? You don't have practice until four, right?"

"Yeah, but we're going to Hoagie Haven first. What's up?"

"Hoagie Haven? Then I guess you won't be able to come shopping with me. There's a sale at Gene's Jeans—forty percent off—and everything I own is really gross," said Miranda, stuffing a handful of papers into one of her notebooks.

"No, I guess I can't go. Scott wants to talk to me about something," Darcy told her. "How long is the sale on? I need some new stuff, too."

"The sale's today and tomorrow. Oh, well, I'll go myself. Call me tonight and tell me if anything *interesting* happens, know what I mean?"

Darcy did. Miranda was the only person in the world who knew about her crush on Scott—at least Darcy hoped she was the only one.

Darcy sighed as she thought about Scott. She got to spend a lot of time with him because she was in the band, but he'd never paid much attention to her—she was just "one of the guys." But now that might all change.

Miranda called goodbye, and Darcy pushed through the heavy doors to find Scott waiting on the school steps.

"Hi," he said, grinning. He shoved his hands into the pockets of his jacket. A gust of icy January wind blew a lock of dark hair over one of his eyes, and his cheeks were reddened by the cold. Darcy thought he'd never looked handsomer.

"Sorry I was late. I had to talk to Miranda," Darcy said.

"That's OK."

She shifted her load of books, and she and Scott walked briskly down Market Street until they reached Hoagie Haven. They slid into a booth, and Scott ordered two Cokes from the waitress, then unzipped his jacket and said, "So, how's everything going?"

"Pretty well. How about with you?" Darcy wasn't very good at small talk, and she wished she could think of something bright or funny to say.

"I'm OK," he said, but he didn't look OK. He was drumming his fingers nervously on the tabletop. It wasn't like Scott to be nervous. Darcy began to feel uncomfortable. The glow she'd felt since he'd asked her to go to Hoagie Haven was rapidly fading.

A couple of girls stopped by their table, leaning close to Scott, and one of them murmured, "Hey, Scott, Jupiter's last concert was really terrific! You were fantastic!" It was as though Darcy weren't there at all; they didn't even glance at her. Scott smiled and thanked them, and they moved on to another booth.

The waitress reappeared with their Cokes, and Darcy took a few sips. Scott kept turning his glass around and around on the table, avoiding her eyes. Finally Darcy said, "You wanted to talk to me about something?"

"Yeah. Yeah, I do." He still didn't meet her gaze.

"So?" asked Darcy. This wasn't at all the way she'd pictured her first date with Scott. She plunged ahead. "Listen, if you don't like the improvisation I did on 'Heartbreaker,' just tell me, OK? I mean, I'll change it if it's not right."

"That's not it," Scott replied. "You're a super keyboardist. Really. And the originals you've written are great. It's just that—"

"Just what?" Darcy was really worried now. She focused her entire attention on Scott's dark, brooding face.

"Well, Jupiter's kind of in a bind. See, we aren't getting enough jobs because we're not any particular style. We have to develop a definite image, and what I've decided is—"

"Yes?" Darcy's heart seemed to have stopped beating. She knew she was about to hear something she wasn't going to like.

"We've decided that the way to go is heavy metal. A real strong sound. We need a rhythm guitarist more than we need a keyboardist."

Stricken, Darcy tore her eyes away from Scott's face and stared down at the tabletop, at the initials carved there by previous customers. "A. L. and T. J. 4-ever," she read. Deep down inside she'd hoped that one day

7

Scott might add, "S. M. and D. B. 4-ever." What a joke.

"You're telling me I'm out, is that it?" she asked tightly.

"Well, that's about it, I guess." Scott took several deep draws on his straw, obviously embarrassed and ill at ease. "I haven't told the other guys yet. I wanted to talk to you first. There's this guitarist I auditioned the other day—"

"You were auditioning guitarists, and you didn't even *tell* me?" Darcy broke in.

"Darcy, I'm sorry. I didn't want to hurt you. It's just that Jupiter's future is more important than the feelings of any one member of the band. The music is really important to me. . . ." He trailed off helplessly.

Darcy pushed her glass away, her eyes brimming with sudden tears. She was taking a backseat to Scott's music again. She swallowed hard and fumbled for the books she'd dropped on the seat beside her. "Sure, I understand." She edged out of the booth, blinking back her tears, determined that Scott would not see how much pain she was feeling. "I'll have somebody drive me over to Tommy's tomorrow after school to pick up my keyboard.

I guess there's no point in my coming to rehearsal this afternoon, is there." It was a question, but she made it a statement.

"I guess not." Scott drained the last of his Coke. "I'm really sorry, Darcy." He looked up at last, briefly meeting her eyes, then glancing away. "I'm really sorry," he repeated. "I'll see you. OK?"

"Yeah, see you around."

Darcy walked slowly out of the restaurant, dazed. She felt as though she'd just been stripped of her identity. If she wasn't Jupiter's keyboardist, who was she? Nobody, that was who.

It was beginning to snow lightly as Darcy walked home, trying to swallow the lump in her throat. Just like that, it was all over. All her dreams of being a musician or of being Scott's girlfriend were shattered. She'd been taken out of the group. Jupiter—or at least Scott—didn't want her anymore. Every now and then she glanced over her shoulder, hoping that maybe he'd changed his mind, that he'd come running after her to tell her he hadn't really meant it. But he had meant it, all right. Darcy was out.

*   *   *

She didn't allow herself to cry until she had closed her bedroom door behind her. Fortunately her mother wasn't home, her father was at work, and her younger sister Carolyn was out as well, so she didn't have to make excuses for hiding out in her room. Darcy flung herself on her bed and sobbed.

It's not fair! she thought miserably. He even said I was *good*. And I *am* good. I hope Jupiter falls flat on its face without me!

Cried out at last, Darcy sat up, pushing damp strands of hair from her swollen eyes. Blindly she reached for a handful of tissues and blew her stuffy nose. Of course she didn't hope Scott's band would fail. She adored Scott, and she didn't really want anything bad to happen to him or to Jupiter. But she was so hurt and humiliated, and she'd had such high hopes for her date with Scott. Some date!

She tossed a crumpled tissue at her wastebasket, and of course, she missed. For some reason that brought on new tears, even though she'd thought she had no more to shed.

A knock on her door brought Darcy up short. She grabbed a handful of tissues and yelled, "What!"

A small voice from the hall said, "Darcy?

You OK? I thought you had practice today. What're you doing home so early?"

It was Darcy's eleven-year-old sister, and she sounded upset. "Yes, I'm OK, and no, I don't have practice, and I'm home because this is where I live. Talk to you later."

"Can I come in?" Carolyn persisted.

"No!" Darcy hollered and was immediately sorry for taking out her anger on her sister. She blew her nose again and called more gently, "Listen, Caro, I just want to be alone for a while. I had kind of a rough day."

Silence from the other side of the door. Finally, "You're *sure* you're OK?"

"I'm sure. Tell Mom I'll be down for supper. I'll tell you all about it later."

Darcy could picture Carolyn standing there, blue eyes troubled, biting her lower lip. Caro always bit her lower lip when she was thinking things out. For a younger sister, Caro was a good kid. She always seemed to be tuned in to Darcy's problems. Not that Darcy had had any really heavy problems until that day. After a brief interval, Darcy heard two brisk knocks signifying goodbye.

Darcy heaved herself up from the bed. She felt as though she weighed about two hundred pounds. It was a great effort to walk over to the wastebasket and drop in the latest batch of damp tissues. In passing she caught a glimpse of herself in the mirror over her dressing table and cringed. Red, puffy face, rumpled clothes—a real washout. *It's a good thing Scott can't see me now*, she thought. Not that he'd care. If he didn't pay attention when she was looking her best, it wouldn't make any difference.

Now that she was on her feet, her first impulse was to call Miranda. Miranda was the only person in the entire world who'd understand how she felt. But Miranda would still be shopping. She'd have to wait until later. With a deep sigh, Darcy slumped into the chair at her desk and rummaged in the lower left-hand drawer where she kept all her personal writings—poems, half-finished short stories, and the words to original tunes she'd composed. She pulled out the file folder marked "Jupiter" and found the lyrics she'd written for her latest song, the one she'd been saving to show Scott. It was a ballad called "Lovesick Girl," and of all Darcy's writings, it was the most personal. She scanned the words thoughtfully.

She's just a lovesick girl,
Playing on her heartstrings,
A lovesick girl who knows what
Giving up your heart brings.
She loves you from afar.
You're her superstar,
And you don't know she's alive!

Darcy had worked up a really super solo for Scott, with lots of good backup from the keyboard and a strong rhythm-and-blues beat. She'd hoped that maybe Jupiter would do the number and that Scott would realize the song was about Darcy's feelings for him. She'd even dreamed of doing the lead vocal herself, though she'd always been relegated to backup vocals in the past. Now he'd never hear it, never know she'd written it for him.

Or would he?

What if she, Darcy Bennett, formed a band of her own? What if she could manage to get a group together and do the number where Scott would be sure to hear it? Better yet, what if her group became a great success, even competing with Jupiter?

An image flashed through her mind of herself in some fabulous outfit, microphone clutched in her hand, belting out those lyrics to a crowd of kids, including Scott. She would be center stage, lit by a follow spot, and the audience would leap to its feet, stamping and yelling out her name. And Scott would be stunned, unable to move, mesmerized by her talent and by the thought that he'd let a diamond slip through his fingers. He'd appreciate her then! And he'd realize that he had loved her all along. Darcy could see him after the concert, looking down at her tenderly and saying, "Darcy, you're the only girl for me. I'm sorry I kicked you out of Jupiter. Please come back. We need you!"

A band, Darcy thought, *but what kind of band?* Not heavy metal. That wasn't her style. Soft rock maybe? Darcy rummaged through the middle drawer of her desk for a yellow legal pad and grabbed a ballpoint pen from the orange juice can covered with gift wrap which had been a Christmas present from Caro two years before.

"Band" she wrote at the top of the page, then paused. A band had to have a name. If Jupiter was becoming supermacho, maybe the thing to do was to create something entirely different. Maybe an all-girl band was the answer!

Darcy scratched out "Band" and substituted "All-Girl Band." But what should she call it? It had to be a name that would instantly let people know that the band was made up of girls. Perhaps a female animal name. . . . The words for female animals popped into her head. "Lioness"? Not bad, but not quite right. "Does"? Forget it! Suddenly Darcy pictured a female fox, bright-eyed and bushy-tailed, sleek and trim. "Vixen!" she shouted and scrawled the word under her heading. "Vixen. That's it!" The fact that there was, as yet, only Darcy herself was a minor matter.

"Just you wait, Scott Maguire," she said to herself and to the photograph of Jupiter that occupied the place of honor in the center of her bulletin board. "This 'lovesick girl' is going to give you a run for your money!"

Chapter Two

By the time Darcy was able to reach Miranda, she'd covered two sheets of her legal pad with ideas about Vixen. To Miranda's cheery "Hello" she responded explosively, "It's about time! What did you do? Go to every store in town? I've been calling and *calling*!"

"Hey, Darcy, cool it! How was I supposed to know you'd be trying to reach me?" Miranda protested. "Aren't you at practice?"

Darcy grimaced. "Hardly. I'm out of the band. Scott fired me this afternoon."

"You're kidding," gasped Miranda.

"I've never been more serious in my life. There we were, sitting in a booth at Hoagie Haven, and Scott told me Jupiter's changing its image. They're going in for a real heavy metal sound, and they don't need a keyboard player anymore, so I'm out."

"Just like that?"

"Just like that," said Darcy.

"You must be wrecked," Miranda said sympathetically. "Scott's got to be out of his mind. You're a great keyboard player, and Jupiter's been doing really well. I always thought Scott was weird. Now I *know* he is!"

"He's not weird, and I'm not wrecked. As a matter of fact, maybe this is a blessing in disguise. I mean I was pretty miserable when he first gave me the news, but then I got this fantastic idea, and you've got to help me."

There was silence on the other end of the line. "What do you mean?" Miranda finally asked.

Immediately Darcy launched into a description of her plans for Vixen. When she paused for a breath, Miranda said, "It sounds super, Darcy, but what does all this have to do with me? I'm about as musical as a bedpost. How do I fit in?"

"You're going to be our manager," Darcy told her. "I always thought Jupiter needed someone to kind of coordinate things, like lining up appearances and getting publicity. We did everything ourselves, and sometimes it got a little hairy. I don't want my band to have to worry about anything except making music. You're the most organized person I know, and you're also my best friend, so naturally I thought of you."

"It might be kind of fun," Miranda said thoughtfully.

"Then you'll do it?" Darcy asked.

"Sure, I'll give it a try. But, Darcy, there's just one little problem."

"What?"

"There's nothing to manage. Vixen doesn't even exist yet."

"Don't be so negative," said Darcy airily. "The first thing we do is set up auditions. You'll put an ad in the *Kennedy Chronicle*, and we'll make up some fliers and put them up around town. I can think of several girls who play rock music, only they've never been in bands because none of the guys would hire them."

"Yeah, there's Lori Berkowitz, and I know a couple of others. It just might work!"

"You bet it's going to work!" cried Darcy.

"It's about time Jupiter discovered they're not the only group at Kennedy High!"

"Listen, if I'm going to do this right, I have to start making plans and laying out schedules. I'll make a few phone calls tonight, and I'm sure I can get an ad in the *Chronicle* on Monday. We'll have to get those fliers made up, too. When do you want to start holding auditions?"

They agreed that the first audition would take place the following Wednesday afternoon in Darcy's basement. They'd need a lead guitarist, a rhythm guitarist, and a drummer. Darcy, of course, would play keyboard.

"I hate to be negative again," said Miranda, "but I can't help wondering where we're going to find a girl who plays drums. I don't know of a single one."

"We don't know every girl at school," Darcy pointed out. "There must be one somewhere. All we can do is wait and see who shows up at the auditions."

But waiting was the last thing in the world she felt like doing. Though the auditions would begin in just one week, it seemed like a year away. When she hung up the phone, Darcy felt at loose ends. There was absolutely nothing she could do to speed up the creation of Vixen, and at the moment, that was the only thing that interested her.

Sighing, she looked around her room. It was a mess, as usual—clothes, records, books, and papers everywhere, particularly on the floor. Her mother had been gearing up for days to an if-you-don't-clean-up-your-room-no-allowance-for-the-next-two-weeks routine. Darcy decided to spend the next half hour cleaning up, first putting her new Police album on the turntable. *If I'm forming my own group, I've got to shape up*, she told herself as she tackled a pile of dirty jeans and T-shirts. *Look out, world, here comes the new Darcy Bennett!*

The photo of Jupiter caught her eye as she passed her desk. Dropping the armful of laundry, she pulled it off the bulletin board. She was about to tear it up when she thought better of it and placed it carefully in the "Jupiter" file. It was such a good picture of Scott. . . .

"Feeling better?" Carolyn asked casually at supper that night.

"Yeah, I'm fine," Darcy responded just as casually.

"Weren't you feeling well today?" asked Mrs. Bennett. "I thought you were home awfully early from practice."

"I didn't have practice," Darcy said and proceeded to fill her family in on the events of the day. Since she'd already told the whole story to Miranda, it was beginning to be a little boring, so she just hit the highlights.

When she'd finished, her father frowned and said, "You mean Scott just kicked you out of the band after we bought you that keyboard and everything? Who does he think he is? That was a major investment."

"I know, Daddy, believe me I know," Darcy said and sighed. "But it won't be a total loss because I'm forming a band of my own." She went on to tell them all about her plans for Vixen, but she didn't think that her father was very impressed.

She was right. "I don't know," he said slowly. "This sounds like a pretty big project and a pretty uncertain one. Your mother and I have gone along with you so far because your music seems to mean so much to you, and you seemed to be getting somewhere with what's-its-name—"

"Jupiter," Carolyn supplied.

21

"Whatever. But if you're not in the band anymore, I don't see why you don't consider doing something more sensible that will lead to a stable future."

Darcy groaned inwardly. She knew her father was going to start in on his favorite topic—how few rock musicians ever made the big time, how uncertain the life was, how unlikely it was she could ever succeed. So she cut him off, saying again, "I know, Daddy. But I've got to prove I'm capable of going off on my own. And I am, I'm sure of it. Besides," she added, "as you said before, you've got a big investment in my keyboard. It'd be a shame to let it go to waste. If everything works out, I'll be making as much money as kids who have part-time jobs, and I'll be able to pay you back for it."

She turned to her mother. "Mom, you understand, don't you? I'll keep up my grades in school—I always have. I need to give this a *try*, at least. And if it doesn't work out, then I'll get a regular after-school job like everyone else."

Mrs. Bennett glanced at her husband, then smiled at Darcy. "I guess it couldn't do any harm. I think it's important for a person to do what makes her happy. Your father and I have always believed in your talents, you know that. And yours, too, Caro," she added, catching her younger daughter's eye. "I say go ahead. We love you, honey. We're behind you a hundred percent."

Darcy grinned. She knew the battle had been won, at least for the moment.

Later that evening as she was trying to concentrate on her geometry homework, Carolyn came into her room, a drawing pad in one hand. "Darcy, I was thinking. You'll need a symbol, a design, for your band, right?" she asked hopefully.

Darcy looked up, glad of the distraction. "We sure will. Do you have some ideas?" Caro was the artistic one in the family. She wanted to be a painter when she grew up—or an architect or a comic book artist, depending on her mood.

"Well, I was thinking about it, and I made some designs. Want to see?" Shyly she handed over the drawing pad, and Darcy took it, flipping through the pages.

"These are really neat," she told her little sister, impressed as always by Caro's imagination and talent. "I think I like the one where the *V* looks like a fox's face. And this one, with the curlicues," she decided. "Why don't you work on those two, and then I'll choose one. We can use it on our posters and fliers for the auditions."

Caro beamed proudly. "Sure!" She was on her way out the door when she paused and turned back. "I think the band's a great idea, Darcy, and I'm glad you aren't sad anymore."

Darcy gave her a wry grin. "Thanks. I'm sorry I yelled at you before. I was just upset. But everything's fine now."

"When you're a big success, Scott'll be sorry he canned you," Caro said. "If you ask me, he's a real jerk."

Darcy bristled. "Scott is *not* a jerk! He's only thinking of the band. He's a really serious musician, and he wants his band to be the best there is. If he thinks Jupiter will have a better chance without me, well, that's his business. You have to be a professional when you're a performer," she added.

"You didn't sound very professional, crying your head off this afternoon," Caro reminded her.

"I was disappointed and surprised, that's all. It was nothing personal," said Darcy, pointedly turning back to her geometry book.

"Sure. Nothing personal. But you'd like Scott to be your boyfriend, wouldn't you?"

Darcy sighed, exasperated. "Caro, it's none of your business, OK? I like your sketches, I'm glad you're excited about my band, but let's not talk about my love life. When you're older, you'll understand."

Caro made a face. "Maybe. All I know is, if a guy I liked pulled what Scott pulled on you, well, I just wouldn't like him anymore, that's all. I'm going, I'm going," she said hastily, edging out the door, intimidated by her older sister's scowl. "And I *still* say he's a jerk!"

She closed the door sharply behind her.

Darcy stared, unseeing, at the pages in front of her. What did Caro know, anyway? Darcy tried to remember five years back, when she had been eleven years old. She couldn't remember a time when she hadn't been secretly in love with Scott. She'd always admired him as the handsome, talented one, the one who knew where he was going and what he wanted to do with his life. He'd been playing the guitar since grade school. Then, when he'd formed Jupiter and chosen her as keyboardist, it seemed she'd taken a giant step toward being the girl in his life. The fact that there had always been other girls hanging around didn't matter. They weren't in the band, and she was.

Except now she wasn't.

But when she was the leader of Vixen, he'd really notice her at last. He'd see her as a person and a musician in her own right, not just somebody he'd rejected because she didn't fit in with his new image and sound. And when he realized she was a star, he'd say, "Darcy, I was wrong." And she'd say—she'd say . . .

Darcy glanced at the clock. If she didn't finish her homework soon, she'd be in real trouble. Anyway, when the time came, she'd know what to say!

At breakfast the next morning, Caro presented Darcy with her two designs for Vixen. And between orange juice and English muffins, Darcy decided she definitely liked the fox-faced one best. Caro, who also enjoyed lettering, volunteered to make half a dozen fliers advertising the auditions, which Darcy and Miranda could post in strategic places.

"Let's see. We'll put one on the main bulletin board outside the office at school and another one in the cafeteria," Darcy said, thinking aloud. "Then we'll stick one up at the Community House and one in Hoagie Haven—all the kids go there."

"How about Record World?" Caro suggested.

"Oh, that's a good idea! And maybe one on the board at the music store. That ought to do it," said Darcy happily. "Thanks, Caro—you're terrific. I'll make sure you get front row seats for all your friends at Vixen's first concert."

Mr. Bennett looked from one daughter to the other, a dubious expression on his face. "I think Darcy got the best of that deal," he told them. "Caro is doing all this work for free tickets to a nonexistent performance of a hypothetical band."

"Oh, Daddy," said Darcy, sighing. "You sound just like Miranda sometimes. Only *she* believes in me!"

"We believe in you, too, dear," her mother said hastily, and her father added, "I always said Miranda had a good head on her shoulders."

"Hey, we'd better get moving, or we'll be late for school," Darcy said, jumping up from the table. She and Caro scrambled for their coats and books, waved goodbye to their parents, dashed out the front door, then went their separate ways.

As she walked to school, Darcy's head was so full of plans for Vixen that she didn't hear the voice calling her, and she jumped when a gloved hand tapped her on the shoulder. Looking up, she saw the friendly face of Pete Esposito, Jupiter's bass guitarist. "Oh, hi, Pete. What's up?" she asked cheerfully.

Pete shrugged and fell into step behind her. "Nothing much. I just wanted to tell you—I mean, about yesterday—we were all real surprised when Scott said you weren't in the band anymore. I'm real sorry, Darcy. I don't think he should have dropped you like that. He's my friend, and he's a good musician, but I think he was wrong."

Darcy smiled. "Thanks, Pete. I have to admit I was pretty shook up when he told me, but I guess he knows what's best for Jupiter. Anyway," she continued in a rush, "I want you to be the first to know—the first in Jupiter to know, that is. I'm starting a band of my own. You'll be hearing a lot about it from now on! Maybe you could just mention it to Scott the next time you see him. Oh, and would you tell Tommy my mother'll be driving me over after school today to pick up my keyboard?"

Pete blinked in surprise. "Your own band? Gee, Darcy, that's great! Sure I'll tell Scott and Tommy. And, good luck. I really mean it."

"Thanks, Pete," Darcy said again, thinking how nice Pete was. She'd miss him a lot, but not as much as she'd miss Scott, of course. *Why couldn't I have fallen in love with Pete instead?* she wondered as they walked along side by side, their breath frosty in the January air. But she knew the answer perfectly well: Scott was special. He was sensitive and a serious musician, much more so than Pete, who was really in it just for kicks and for the recognition he got from the girls at school.

Darcy realized that Pete had been talking and she hadn't heard a word he'd said, so she concentrated on paying attention to him and on keeping up her end of the conversation. Soon they were joined by other kids on the way to Kennedy High, and Darcy let the chatter swirl around her, retreating once more into her daydreams. But they wouldn't be dreams for long. Soon Vixen would be a reality. Her very own band! She could hardly wait.

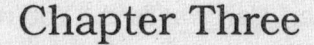

Chapter Three

The tall, large girl in skintight jeans tucked her guitar pick into her back pocket and rested her Fender Stratocaster on one hip. "Well, that's it," she said. Her grin was half-nervous, half-proud. "Like I told you, I've studied classical guitar for years, but I really want to get into a rock band. I bet I've auditioned for every group in town, but it's always the same thing—they say I'm good, but they won't give me a chance because I'm a girl."

Darcy leaped up from her seat at the electric piano and switched off the tape of the Stones that had been playing while Lori auditioned. She was beaming, delighted with the other girl's performance. Lori Berkowitz was head and shoulders above the other girls who had auditioned the past three days for Vixen's lead guitarist. Darcy looked over at Miranda, who was sipping soda out of a can, curled up in a threadbare armchair that had once graced the Bennetts' living room but had long since been relegated to the basement.

Miranda grinned and nodded. "What did I tell you?" she said smugly. "Lori's great!"

"Terrific," Darcy agreed. "You're just what we've been looking for. If you want to be Vixen's lead guitarist, you've got it!"

Lori relaxed and lifted her guitar strap over her head, then gently placed her Strat into its case on the floor at her feet.

"Fantastic!" She sighed. "I love your idea, Darcy. An all-girl band. It's about time." She flopped down on the equally threadbare sofa, folding her long arms across her chest. "I thought Beth Ferguson would be here today. Didn't you say she's your bass player?"

"Yes, but she had to go to the dentist. She's going to do some lead vocals, too. Do you know Beth?" Darcy asked.

"Kind of. She's in a couple of my classes. Funny, I never knew she played bass."

"Her brother taught her," Miranda said,

"and when he went away to college, he left her his old bass and an amplifier he didn't need."

"So you've found a bass player and a lead guitarist, and you're doing keyboard and the rest of the vocals. If you're not looking for a rhythm guitarist, all you need—all *we* need," Lori amended, "is a drummer, right?"

"Right," said Darcy and grimaced. "That's our big problem."

"I warned you," said Miranda, taking the last swig of her soda and tossing the empty can into the milk crate that served as a wastebasket. "Girl drummers are as scarce as hens' teeth, as my grandmother would say."

Darcy smiled and turned to Lori hopefully. "You don't know of any girls who play drums, do you? Without a drummer, we're sunk."

Lori frowned. "I can't think of anybody. Not many girls take up drums."

Darcy sank down onto the sofa beside Lori, wincing as a broken spring poked her in the rear. "We *have* to find a drummer."

Just then Mrs. Bennett called down the stairs, "Darcy, there's a boy on the phone asking for you. His name is Carl Bradley. Do you want to talk to him?"

"Oh, no, not another one!" said Darcy, groaning.

"What do you mean, 'another one'?" Lori asked.

"Oh, a lot of guys think it's funny to come up to me in school, or call me, talking in squeaky voices and saying they want to audition for my all-girl band. It's a real pain," Darcy told her.

"Very immature," added Miranda.

"Darcy! Did you hear me?" Mrs. Bennett shouted.

"Yeah, I'll be right there," Darcy shouted back. She got to her feet and shrugged. "I don't even *know* a Carl Bradley. I'd better talk to him and see what he wants."

She bounded up the steps and took the receiver from her mother's hand.

"Hello?"

"Hi, is this Darcy Bennett?" The voice was definitely not squeaky. In fact, it was deep and pleasant.

"Yes, who's this?" Darcy asked suspiciously.

"My name's Carl Bradley. You don't know me, but I saw your flier, and I'd like to audition for Vixen."

Darcy rolled her eyes. "Look, I'm getting really sick of this routine. I don't know who put you up to it, but if this is a joke, I'm not laughing."

"It's no joke," the voice responded calmly. "I know Vixen's supposed to be strictly female, but I'm a pretty good drummer. I play in the Kennedy orchestra and band, and I'd really like to be part of a group."

He sounded serious, but Darcy wasn't convinced. "I'm really only looking for girls," she explained. Suddenly an image flashed into her mind of a good-looking boy with blond hair, half hidden behind the kettledrums at the last Kennedy orchestra concert she'd attended. She recalled thinking she must not have seen him before because if she had, she would have remembered him.

"I appreciate your calling and all that, but I'm afraid I'm just not interested in guys— for the band, that is," she quickly corrected.

Apparently Carl was not fazed in the least. "I just figured you might be having some trouble finding a girl drummer and you might be willing to stretch a point. I'd really like to audition for you. Before we moved to Fairfield in November, I played drums in a couple of rock bands in Philadelphia. Nothing big—high-school stuff—but we performed a lot."

Darcy felt herself beginning to waver. But she'd only been auditioning for three days, and surely she could find a girl drummer who'd be right for Vixen. It was only a matter of time before she showed up. Still, Darcy was eager to get her band together fast.

"Darcy? You there?"

"Yes, sorry, I've just been thinking." She paused. "Are you *sure* you're serious?"

"I'm serious," Carl replied, and his voice sounded so sincere she had to believe him.

It was all very tempting, but finally she said, "Listen, Carl, I'm really sorry. Vixen's got to be the kind of band I want, and that means no guys. I haven't given up on finding a girl drummer, yet. But thanks for calling, anyway."

"OK," said Carl. "Could I give you my number, though, in case you change your mind?"

Darcy sighed. "All right. But don't count on it." She wrote the number down on the pad by the phone, then said, "Bye. Thanks for calling."

"My pleasure," he answered and hung up.

" 'My pleasure,' " Darcy repeated, smiling

a little. It was an old-fashioned thing to say, but kind of nice.

"Was that someone from school, honey?" her mother asked. "I didn't recognize the name."

"He's new here. Would you believe he actually, seriously wanted to audition for Vixen?"

"Not a joke?"

"He said not, and he sounded serious," Darcy said thoughtfully.

"Hmm," murmured Mrs. Bennett, lifting the cover of a pot on the stove and stirring the bubbling stew with a slotted spoon. "We'll be eating in about half an hour. Your father's late tonight. You're finished with the auditions, aren't you? You know how he hates the noise. He's sure the vibrations are going to loosen the plaster on the ceiling."

"Oh, *Mom!* Nobody's house ever collapsed because some kids were playing loud music in the basement. *Really!*"

"There's always a first time," her mother said.

Just then Miranda's frizzy head appeared in the doorway to the basement. "Hi, Mrs. B.

Darcy, you coming back down? Lori has to leave, and so do I. Who was on the phone?"

"Just a guy from school, a drummer." Darcy followed her down the steps. "He plays percussion in the orchestra and band."

Lori, who was putting on her ski jacket, said, "No kidding? He really wanted to audition?"

"No kidding—I think. But I told him absolutely no guys in Vixen!"

"Right!" Miranda said firmly. "What did your mother say his name was?"

"Carl Bradley. His family just moved to town in November."

"Carl Bradley . . ." Lori reflected, picking up her guitar case. "I've seen him around. Isn't he a senior, kind of tall, blond, very good-looking?"

Darcy shrugged. "I've seen him in the orchestra. I guess you'd call him good-looking, if you go for that type."

"Who doesn't go for that type?" asked Lori and giggled.

Miranda scowled at her. "Lori, you don't seriously think Darcy should have let him audition, do you? I mean, Vixen is strictly for girls, right?"

"Right, sure," Lori agreed hastily. "All I said was he's attractive. Just because we don't want boys in the band doesn't mean we don't appreciate them, does it?"

"Of course not," said Darcy, thinking of Scott. "Hey, back to business, gang. Lori, we'll be auditioning drummers next Wednesday, Thursday, and Friday. Beth's coming. Are you available?"

"Absolutely! I bet by the end of next week we'll be all set."

Lori and Miranda let themselves out the side door, and as Darcy closed the door behind them, she hoped that Lori's prediction would turn out to be the truth.

Exactly one week later, the same group was gathered in the Bennetts' basement, with the addition of Beth Ferguson, a slender, delicate blond who looked as though she belonged behind a harp rather than a Gibson Ripper bass guitar. All four girls were sprawled on various pieces of cast-off furniture, surrounded by instruments and amps, and all four were looking very glum. Miranda broke what had been a long, strained silence by saying, "Let's face it, girls. There is not one female drummer in Fairfield, Pennsylvania. We've held six days of auditions, and we've come up with exactly zilch."

"Not quite," Beth pointed out in her soft, flutelike voice that indicated none of the power it could produce when singing. "There was that friend of Darcy's sister's, that kid with the glasses."

"Yeah, Betsy Epler." Darcy sighed. "She's good, but she's too much younger than the rest of us."

Silence fell again.

Finally Miranda, who had been looking through the notes on her clipboard, tossed it aside and said, "Well, as far as I'm concerned, I've done the best I could. Without a drummer, there's no Vixen, and if there's no Vixen, I'm out of a job, and so are the rest of you. It was a great idea, Darcy, but I guess it's just not going to work."

"Don't *say* that!" wailed Darcy. Only that very day, she'd run into Scott in the hall at school, and when he'd asked her how her band was coming, she'd told him airily that everything was fine and they'd be performing very soon. He had seemed impressed and had even mentioned Kennedy High's annual Battle of the Bands. He'd asked her if she was going to enter Vixen, and she'd said, "Of course." Now she'd look like a jerk if the whole thing fizzled out.

"What about that guy?" Lori asked suddenly, leaning forward.

"What guy?"

"You know, the one who called you last Friday. The cute one who plays in the orchestra."

"Oh, Carl What's-his-name," said Darcy without interest. "So?"

"Well, he's a drummer, isn't he? And he wants to get into a band. And we're a band who needs a drummer."

"Carl Bradley? You mean that neat new guy?" asked Beth eagerly. "He's cute! Of course, he's not a girl, but a drummer's a drummer, right?"

"Wrong!" Darcy snapped. "The whole point of Vixen is that it's an all-girl group. And I don't think Carl could pass for a girl."

Miranda frowned. "So what?"

"What do you mean 'so what'?" asked Darcy, annoyed. "If we let a boy into the band, we'll lose our individuality. We'll be just like any other group."

"Not really," said Beth, pushing back a strand of hair. "You have to consider the alternatives. It's a question of the survival of Vixen, and if Vixen can't survive without a guy, we'd better consider stretching a point."

Which was exactly what Carl had said a week before, Darcy remembered. She looked at Lori, then at Miranda. Neither of them had as big a stake in Vixen as she did, but they did want the band to be a success. "Well, maybe—" she said, faltering.

"Not maybe—definitely!" cried Miranda, snatching up her clipboard and making a quick note. "You have his phone number. It wouldn't hurt to let him audition. Maybe he's terrible. Maybe that's the real reason why he hasn't been able to hook up with any other band. But you'll never know until you hear him, right?"

"I guess so," Darcy agreed reluctantly. "If he's really bad, we're no worse off than we are right now."

"Terrific!" cried Lori. "Why don't you call him right now?"

"Now?" squawked Darcy, suddenly apprehensive. "Maybe he's not home. Maybe he has a job after school—"

"Darcy, *call him*," whispered Beth, touching her arm. "If he still wants to audition, I'm available tomorrow or Sunday. What about you, Lori? Miranda?"

Both girls nodded. Outnumbered, Darcy realized the only thing to do was to make the call.

"OK, I'll do it," she said after a moment's consideration. "But he may have changed his mind. Or it may have been a joke after all."

"*Call him*," all three girls said in unison, and Darcy had no choice but to trudge up the stairs and face the telephone.

She was glad her mother was vacuuming, and that Caro wasn't home. It would be hard enough to call—she didn't need an audience.

Carl's number was still on the pad by the phone. She dialed, and no one answered on the first four rings. She was about to hang up, but on the fifth ring a voice answered, a voice she immediately recognized as Carl's.

"Hi. Carl?"

"Yes?" His voice was as pleasant as she remembered it, and she relaxed a little.

"This is Darcy Bennett. The girl from Vixen," she added in case he didn't remember.

"Sure, I thought I recognized your voice. What's up?"

"Well, I was thinking, and if you really want to audition for us and you're free over the weekend, it's OK. Saturday or Sunday, my place, around two or three o'clock." Her parents were going to be out both Saturday and Sunday afternoons, she recollected, so her father wouldn't complain about the noise if Carl decided to come.

"Great! How about tomorrow at two-thirty?" he suggested.

Darcy swallowed. "That'll be fine. We'll see you then."

When she returned to the basement, the girls were delighted with her news.

"What harm can it do?" asked Lori cheerfully. "If he's terrible, no problem. If he's good, we've got a drummer, and we've got Vixen, right?"

"And if he's awful, at least we'll have gotten to know him a little," Beth added. "He's so attractive."

But Darcy wasn't sure. After Lori and Beth left, she decided to talk to Miranda. "I can't help wondering what'll happen if we let a boy into the band," she said. "Say he's really fantastic, and we decide to use him. Beth and Lori have their eyes on him already, and they haven't even *met* him yet. All we need is two girls competing for one guy. It'll break Vixen up for sure. Not only that, what if he turns out to be a real take-over person, the kind of boy who has to be in charge no matter what?"

"Like Scott, you mean," Miranda suggested shrewdly.

"Well, yes, kind of," Darcy admitted. "I've never met a boy who could sit back and let a girl run things, and Vixen's *my* band. I don't want some stranger muscling in."

"Gimme a break!" Miranda shouted. "He hasn't even set foot in the house, and already you're making up all kinds of problems. What's the matter with you, anyway? I thought the most important thing was to get a good group together."

"It *is* the most important thing," Darcy agreed. "I'm just not sure this is the way to go about it."

Miranda was perched on an amp, hands on her hips. "Well, the way I see it, we have three options. Number one, we let Carl audition, and if he doesn't work out, we audition other boys. Number two, we take your sister's friend." Darcy made a face. "Number three, you call up Carl, cancel the audition, forget Vixen, and chalk it up to experience. If you want to know how I feel, I vote for number one. What about you?"

Darcy ran her fingers over the keys of her electric piano, silently playing a scale. After a moment's consideration, she looked up and met Miranda's steady gaze with a rueful grin.

"I guess it's unanimous," she finally said.

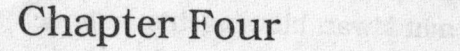

Chapter Four

It was Caro who answered the doorbell when it rang the next day promptly at two-thirty, since Darcy, Lori, and Beth were practicing in the basement.

"Hi," she said. "Are you Carl?"

"Yup," he replied. "But you're not Darcy, are you?"

Caro shook her head. "No, I'm her sister Carolyn. Darcy's downstairs with the rest of the group."

"So I hear," said Carl. "My drum kit's out in my car. Should I bring it in this way, or is there another entrance?"

"You'd better bring it around to the side. I'll tell Darcy you're here."

As Carl went back down the path to his old van and began unloading his drums, Caro dashed to the basement stairs, flicking the light switch on and off to get the girls' attention. When the music trailed off, she called down, "Carl's here! Unlock the side door!"

Darcy ran up the stairs and unbolted the door, to find Carl standing outside with a snare drum, high-hat and tom-tom. The icy wind was blowing his hair across his face, and his eyes were sparkling. Darcy caught her breath. He was as handsome as she'd remembered, maybe even more so now that she saw him close up. *So what?* she asked herself sternly. *The main thing is, is he good?*

"I'm Darcy Bennett," she said out loud. "Need a hand with those?" She indicated the equipment, aware of Lori and Beth crowding behind her, practically breathing down her neck.

"I'm Lori."

"I'm Beth."

Their voices came almost in unison, accompanied by dazzling smiles. Before Carl could reply, they had edged around Darcy and were picking up the drums and cymbals, bringing them into the basement.

Carl's eyes met Darcy's for a brief moment; they flashed with an amusement that did not escape her. "I'll get the bass drum from the car," he said, smiling. His teeth were white and straight.

"Just bring it right down into the basement," she told him, turning away. She wasn't going to offer to help him, not after Lori and Beth had practically melted at his feet. She was the leader of this group, and he'd better realize that right away.

"Well, here we go," she said to Miranda, who was curled up in her favorite chair, making notes on her ever-present clipboard. "I just hope Beth and Lori can pull themselves together enough to act like musicians and not like groupies," she added in a whisper, glancing apprehensively at them.

Darcy needn't have worried. As soon as Carl set up his drum kit, Lori and Beth behaved professionally. After the four of them had run through all the popular songs Darcy had chosen for Vixen's repertoire, plus a few improvisations on originals she had composed, she had to admit that Carl was a super drummer. She could tell from the other girls' reactions, including Caro's, who had crept down the stairs to watch, that they felt the same way.

Everybody was relaxing with cans of soda, listening to a Rolling Stones album, when Darcy turned to Carl and said as noncommittally as possible, "You're pretty good."

"Pretty good! He's unbelievable!" cried Lori. "Why haven't you gotten involved with another band?" she asked Carl. "Some of the local groups have really terrible drummers. How come you're available?"

Carl shrugged. "My family just moved here a couple months ago. I joined the orchestra and band at Kennedy, but Vixen's ad was the first one I've seen. I'd heard about Jupiter, but I've never been to one of their concerts or anything. They're supposed to be the biggest band around."

"Darcy used to play keyboard for them," said Miranda proudly. "But they decided to replace her with a rhythm guitarist, and that's why she's forming her own band."

"Tough luck," Carl said sympathetically, looking over at Darcy. "Also bad judgment. You're the best keyboardist I've ever played with, and those originals are really good."

Darcy felt herself blushing and couldn't

suppress a warm feeling of pleasure. "Thanks," she said softly.

"Well?" prodded Miranda.

"Well, what?" Darcy retorted, though she knew very well what Miranda meant.

"Well, I think we have to make a decision. And you're the boss," Miranda pointed out.

Darcy felt a knot tightening in her stomach. It was all up to her. The success or failure of Vixen depended on her. She looked at Carl, noticing in spite of herself how the color of his Shetland sweater matched the startling blue of his eyes.

After a brief pause, she said, "I say yes." Lori let out a whoop, while Beth said a very breathy, "Terrific!"

"But I have to warn you," Darcy told Carl, "you're probably going to get a lot of kidding from the guys at school. Everybody knows Vixen's supposed to be strictly female."

Carl grinned. "I think I can handle it. And I have three sisters, so I'm used to being outnumbered. As far as I'm concerned, it's a deal. Shake, boss!"

He leaned forward, stretching out his right hand. Darcy took it in hers—and shrieked as a spark of static electricity made her jerk her hand away. Everyone laughed, including Darcy.

On the second try, Carl's big, warm hand closed firmly around hers in a formal handshake. She'd done it. Vixen was a reality, not just a dream. Darcy felt she'd taken the first major step toward showing Scott Maguire she could manage perfectly well without Jupiter. Come to think of it, maybe having Carl in the band would turn out to be an asset in terms of making Scott sit up and take notice. It certainly wouldn't hurt for him to see her working closely with another boy, particularly a boy as talented and attractive as Carl.

"OK, that's settled," said Miranda briskly. "Now, how about setting up a rehearsal schedule? The sooner you get your act together, the sooner I can start lining up gigs. And if you want to enter the Battle of the Bands, you'll need all the performing experience you can get."

For the next half hour, Darcy, Carl, Lori, and Beth juggled times and dates, finally working out a schedule that accommodated Carl's band and orchestra practice, Darcy's piano lessons, Lori's part-time job, and Beth's baby-sitting commitments.

"The way I see it," Darcy said at last, "is that if we work really hard, we ought to be ready to perform by the beginning of March, if we practice every weekend as well as after school. Miranda, I want you to contact every school in Fairfield, and even in York and Lancaster. Let them know we'll be available for anything. And get in touch with community organizations, church groups, *everybody*. We'll play for dances, fund raisers, private parties, you name it. Beth, you're getting a lot of feedback on your amp. Maybe you ought to have it checked out. And, Lori, if you need new strings, you'd better get them right away." Her face was flushed with excitement. "There won't be anything that's second-rate about Vixen!"

Carl looked at her, a quizzical expression on his face. "This really means a lot to you, doesn't it?" he said quietly as the girls were putting on their jackets.

"Yes. Yes, it does," Darcy admitted.

"Because of Jupiter?" he continued, and Darcy tore her eyes away from his, flustered at his shrewd perception.

"That has something to do with it, I guess," she said. "But it's also because I really want to do my own thing. Until today, Vixen was only a dream. And now it's real. We're going to be a big success, I just know it!"

"What if we're not?" Carl's words were like icy water flung in her face.

Angrily Darcy spun around. "What do you mean, 'What if we're not?' We will be. We have to be!"

Carl stood up from the sofa he had been comfortably slumped in. "Hey, don't bite my head off. It's just that for every band that makes it, there are dozens, maybe hundreds, that don't." She looked away from him again. "The important thing is that we really like what we're doing, right? Everything else is gravy."

Darcy smiled ruefully. "It's funny. You sound just like my parents. My dad keeps saying how tough the music world is, and my mom keeps telling him that what matters is doing something a person really enjoys."

"I guess that's because I've heard it all before, from *my* folks," said Carl. "And they're right, all of them. Don't get me wrong, Darcy. I want this group to succeed, too. When I do something, I do it one hundred percent. But

I'd hate to lose sight of the fact that this is supposed to be fun, not do-or-die competition with other bands."

Darcy nodded. "Sure. I understand. I promise I won't go off the deep end."

Carl's smile was warm. "If you do, mind if I pull you back?" he asked. Darcy, smiling too, shook her head.

He grabbed his jacket then and shrugged into it. "Anybody need a ride? My van's outside."

Beth, Lori, and, somewhat to Darcy's surprise, even Miranda, took him up on his offer. A few minutes later they were gone, leaving Darcy shivering by the open door. As she watched them go down the path, laughing and talking, Beth suddenly slipped on a patch of ice and grabbed for Carl's arm. Darcy noticed that she kept it, too, and Carl didn't seem to mind at all.

"He's a really good drummer, isn't he?" said Caro, who had come to stand beside her. "I guess if you couldn't use Betsy, he'll be OK. He's really handsome, too—like somebody on TV."

Darcy groaned. "Not you, too!"

"What do you mean?" Caro asked innocently. "Do *you* like him?"

"Of course I *like* him," Darcy explained patiently, "but not the way you mean. He's a good drummer, and he seems like a nice person, but don't get any ideas. Carl's not my type." Darcy closed the side door and locked it, then went up the steps to the kitchen, Caro at her heels.

"I think he's nicer than Scott," Caro continued. "I guess it's true what they say."

"What do they say?" Darcy asked absently, not really paying attention.

"That love is blind. I read that somewhere."

"Oh, Caro! Do me a favor—shut up!" Darcy said snappishly. "Love has nothing to do with it. The only thing on my mind right now is Vixen. I couldn't care less about romance."

"Hmph," said Caro and retreated upstairs.

Darcy followed her slowly, wondering if she'd done the right thing by letting Carl into the band. Already he seemed to be creating problems, even with her little sister. Then she shrugged. As she'd told Caro, Vixen was the only thing that mattered. Well, Vixen and Scott.

* * *

The rehearsal schedule Darcy and Miranda had set up was truly rigorous, leaving little time for anything else. But as the days became weeks, the band was shaping up beautifully, in spite of the fact that both Beth and Lori were obviously falling all over themselves to impress Carl. Carl, however, didn't seem to notice. He treated them all like sisters, and he never once tried to take over as leader of the group or to question Darcy's authority. He'd make an occasional suggestion, which Darcy usually found valuable, but when she disagreed, her decision stood. And if the other guys at Kennedy gave him a hard time about being Vixen's token male, he never mentioned it.

In the meantime Miranda was trying her best to line up work for Vixen, without success. Wherever she went, Jupiter had been there before her, and Jupiter's reputation was so good that the schools and community groups she approached said they preferred to hire them than take a chance on a new, untried group.

"I don't know what it *is* with these people,"

Miranda said one afternoon after school when she and Darcy were sharing a pizza at Dino's. "I give them a big pitch and tell them how great you guys are, but they say if they can't hire Jupiter, they don't want anybody. It's getting me down."

"Don't worry," Darcy mumbled through a large bite of pizza. "Sooner or later we're going to get our first gig, and when we do everybody's going to be knocking each other down to hire us. The first one's always the hardest. You're doing a terrific job, you really are."

"Yeah, a terrific job of wearing out my Nikes tramping from one place to another, getting rejected. It's bad for my ego," said Miranda earnestly. "I know it's not *me* they're rejecting, but I'm beginning to feel like I have bubonic plague or something. I don't know how much longer I can take it."

"It'll happen. I know it will. All we need is one engagement, and we'll be on our way." Darcy was sure it was only a matter of time before Vixen would be climbing toward fame and fortune, or at least toward local recognition. And when that happened, Scott would be at her side, telling her how wonderful she was.

Not that she'd seen much of him lately. She passed him in the halls and sometimes they would chat briefly, usually about Jupiter's latest triumph. He hadn't exactly been knocking down her door with offers for dates. On the other hand, he didn't seem to be seeing anyone else on a steady basis, although the Jupiter groupies were always hanging around him, hoping for a glance or a word. *I won't do that*, she told herself fiercely. *If he doesn't come to me, I'll be darned if I'll go to him!*

"You're drifting," said Miranda. "Listen, it's all very well to talk about that first engagement, but what I've been telling you is I can't get Vixen signed up for *anything*. Nobody wants a band unless they've got a reputation, and you can't get a reputation until somebody hires you. It's a vicious circle."

Darcy sprinkled her last slice of pizza with garlic salt and frowned. Finally she said thoughtfully. "Hire. You said 'hire.' "

"Yeah. Like for money. Nobody wants to risk their money on—"

"What if we performed for free?" Darcy asked eagerly. "Like a showcase. No money. I bet we'd get something in a minute if we didn't charge. Just the first one. After that, we'd expect to be paid the going rate. It would be worth it in the long run!"

"How do you think the rest of the band would feel about that?" Miranda asked doubtfully. "You've all been working so hard for so long, and Lori's even cut down on her hours at Woolworth's so she can come to all those rehearsals."

"It's an investment in the future," Darcy insisted. "I'm sure they'll see it my way. Come on, Miranda, isn't there anybody you've contacted who'd want a band if they didn't have to pay them?"

"Well—" Miranda pulled her clipboard out of her school bag and consulted a list. "The Community House has scheduled a dance for the first Saturday in March, and they were going to use Hit and Run because Jupiter's so expensive. But the lady I talked to said even Hit and Run's rates were pretty steep. I guess I could—"

"Ask her!" commanded Darcy. "No fee, just free soda and snacks for the band. Tell her we'll donate our services! And don't worry about the others. I'll explain. It'll work!"

Miranda didn't seem completely convinced, but she agreed to give it a try. "I just hope you know what you're doing," she added.

Darcy giggled. "Me, too!"

Chapter Five

It took very little persuasion for Darcy to convince Beth, Lori, and Carl that an engagement that didn't pay was better than no engagement at all. They were all eager to show off Vixen's abilities. Miranda spoke to Mrs. Andretti at the Community House, and she was more than happy to sign up the unknown band for the March dance. Darcy was flying high. They actually had their first job!

The next Friday afternoon the group was gathered in Darcy's basement, rehearsing their numbers, when Caro bounced down the basement stairs and signaled wildly to Darcy.

"What's up, Caro? You know we don't want to be interrupted when we're practicing."

"Yeah, well, I just thought you might like to know you have a visitor." Caro glanced over her shoulder. "Scott's here. He asked if he could watch a rehearsal, and I didn't know what to tell him."

Darcy's heart leaped, then started hammering crazily, but she forced herself to appear calm and cool. "Sure. Tell him to come on down."

Scott appeared behind Caro, his hands shoved in the pockets of his black leather jacket. "Hi, Darcy," he said. "Mind if I sit in?"

"No, of course not," said Darcy. "Have a seat." They were just about to play "Lovesick Girl." It would be the first time he'd heard the song Darcy had written for him. "How's Jupiter doing?" she asked casually.

"Great, really great. I hear you're going to be playing at the Community House, so I thought I'd check out the competition." Scott unzipped his jacket and sank down onto the battered sofa. "Just pretend I'm not here," he said.

Quivering inside, Darcy gave the downbeat, and the group began to play. Darcy's voice rang out loud and clear on the vocal, and to her ears, at least, Vixen had never sounded better. As she sang she wondered if Scott would guess she'd written the song for him. Halfway through the number, though, she caught Carl's eye and blushed and looked away. If Scott didn't realize the song was about her feelings toward him, she got the uncomfortable feeling that Carl did. He seemed to have a way of knowing things that weren't explicitly stated. Sometimes Darcy felt he knew her better than she knew herself, and she wasn't sure she liked that.

They played several other numbers after "Lovesick Girl," and when they'd finished, Scott nodded slowly. "That's good, Darcy. In fact, it's great. You've got a terrific group here."

Again Darcy blushed, much to her embarrassment. To cover up she introduced Scott to the others. Lori and Beth knew him from school and Jupiter, although they had never talked to him, and they were thrilled to have the chance. Carl and Scott shook hands and talked for a few minutes as well. Later, as Lori, Beth, and Carl were getting ready to leave, Scott came over to Darcy.

"Hey, how about a hamburger? We could

go to McDonald's. I've hardly seen you the last few weeks."

Darcy was stunned. "Sure," she whispered. "I'd like that." She turned to the others. "See you tomorrow afternoon, right?"

"Right, slave driver," Lori said, then laughed.

When Carl and the girls had left, Darcy ran upstairs to get her jacket and, hardly believing what was happening, walked with Scott to McDonald's. When they were seated at a table, their hamburgers and drinks in front of them, Scott said, "I'm really impressed. Vixen sounds great."

"Thanks," replied Darcy, barely tasting her food. "How did you like my new song?"

" 'Lovesick'? Is that yours?"

"Yes, I wrote it," Darcy said, trying to sound casual. "What did you think of it?"

"I liked it. I liked it a lot. Your vocal, too. How come you never sang for Jupiter?"

Darcy raised her head, eyes flashing. "You never let me!" she retorted. "In Jupiter I was always backup. But with Vixen—"

"With Vixen, you're in control, right?" asked Scott with his familiar lopsided grin.

Darcy felt herself melting as she looked into his eyes. "Yeah, something like that."

"Well, you're doing fine."

Three girls stopped at their table. One, a slender blond, leaned over and draped an arm around Scott's neck. "Hi, Scottie. How's it going?"

"Scottie"! Darcy thought. *Really gross!*

"Great, Tricia. Thanks," said Scott, putting down his hamburger.

"We're all going to be right in front when you play at Sunshine's tonight," she said.

"Cool," said Scott with a little smile. "I hope you like the concert."

"Hi, Marcy," one of the other girls ventured, turning to Darcy.

"That's Darcy," she snapped, bristling.

After a few minutes, the girls headed for the door, and Scott focused his attention on Darcy again.

"Hey, I thought Vixen was supposed to be an all-girl band. Couldn't find a drummer?"

"Nope," said Darcy, and she launched into the story of Caro's friend Betsy and finally wound up by saying, "So when Carl wanted to audition, I figured a guy drummer was better than no drummer at all."

"He's good," said Scott. "Seems funny, though, a guy trying out for a girls' band. I guess he must have auditioned for all the other groups and nobody would have him, so he gave Vixen a shot."

A little shaken by Scott's evaluation, Darcy said, "You just told me he's good."

"Sure, but he's a loser, Darcy. Don't you think that if he were really good, he'd have gotten into one of the established bands like Risk or Hit and Run? Forget Jupiter—Tommy's the greatest. But if Carl's such a hotshot, he wouldn't have been available. Come on, admit it."

"I will not," cried Darcy. The last thing she wanted was for Scott to think she'd settled for second best. "I'll admit I thought it was a joke when he called. A lot of guys thought it was funny to try to pass themselves off as girls over the phone when we were having our first auditions. But Carl was new in town. He hadn't been here long enough to audition for other groups. And he was serious. So I told him he could try out, and—"

"And you took him," Scott finished for her. "I don't blame you. But he's kind of a wimp."

Darcy, trying to remain calm, said tightly, "I don't think so. And I really don't care. A drummer is a drummer." As she said the words, she was conscious of a sinking sensation in her stomach. Winning Scott's approval was pretty important to her, and this was not exactly the way to get it. She wanted Scott to think she was making good decisions where Vixen was concerned. Somehow their conversation had gone all wrong.

"Hey," said Scott, changing the subject and engulfing her in his big, dark brown eyes. That irresistible grin curled at the corners of his mouth. "How'd you like to go to the movies Saturday night? Some of the guys from Jupiter are going to see *The Return of the Vampire* at the cheapies down on Austin Street. Want to come?"

"With *you*?" she asked, trying to keep her voice in its proper register. "On Saturday *night*? But doesn't Jupiter have a concert or something? I thought you were booked solid."

Scott looked away and waved at a friend passing by. "Just about, but this one Saturday night we have free, probably the only one in the next few months. Everybody's got to relax sometime. What about it? Or do you have a date with your new drummer?"

Darcy shook her head vehemently. "No. No, I'm free."

Scott reached out and took her hand. If Darcy had been a fainting person, she would have passed out right then and there. As it was, she tried to connect her tongue with her brain. At last she managed to say, "That'd be fine. When will you pick me up?"

"How about seven-thirty? The show starts at eight." He squeezed her hand briefly, then dropped it, but Darcy could feel the warmth afterward.

"OK," she said. "I'll be ready."

"Great. See you then." Scott tucked his paper napkin into his soda cup. "You ready to go?"

Darcy nodded, and they stood up.

As they walked out the door together, Darcy was ecstatic. She had a real date with Scott Maguire! It was what she had dreamed about. All the Jupiter groupies were going to eat their hearts out.

She'd wear her new Jordache jeans and the lavender sweater she'd gotten for her sixteenth birthday. On the way home, she'd stop at the drugstore for a bottle of that fantastic apple shampoo, the stuff Miranda used that made her hair smell so nice. And she'd use her mother's Chanel N° 5 cologne. It was a very sophisticated scent. Probably none of the other girls Scott knew used it. Then, after Saturday, he'd always associate the smell of Chanel N° 5 with Darcy Bennett. It would be her signature. She'd ask for a bottle of it for her next birthday.

At the corner she called goodbye to Scott, then walked home, wrapped cozily in dreams of her future with him.

Chapter Six

Darcy found it practically impossible to concentrate on the music at Vixen's Saturday afternoon rehearsal. Her mind kept wandering to Scott and their date that night. It was Lori who finally said, after Darcy had missed yet another cue, "I've heard of sleepwalking, but this is the first time I've ever seen anybody sleep*playing*! Darcy, what's with you? You're really out of it."

"I'm sorry. You're right. I just can't seem to get my head together," Darcy looked at her watch. It was three-thirty and she'd planned on rehearsing for at least another hour. "Suppose we call it quits for now. I promise I'll be in better shape tomorrow."

Beth widened her green eyes. "I can't believe what I'm hearing! Come on, gang, before she changes her mind!"

The girls began putting away their instruments, and Carl came up beside Darcy. "You feel all right?" he asked, concern in his voice.

"Yes, I'm fine. Really," Darcy assured him, flashing a smile. "It's just that I have something else on my mind, something besides Vixen for a change!"

Carl nodded. "That's good. Sometimes I think you're taking all this too seriously. Sure, the band's important, but so's your personal life. When you're not having any fun, you get kind of uptight." He paused. "I don't mean you, personally—just people in general."

"I know what you mean," said Darcy ruefully. "I've been driving you all pretty hard. Myself, too. Thanks for putting up with me."

Carl laughed. "You're not all that hard to put up with."

Darcy's eyes met his, and she felt a funny little shiver run down her spine. She'd never known that blue eyes could be so warm. . . .

"Carl, you ready to go?" called Beth impatiently.

"Sure. Be with you in a minute." Carl scooped up his jacket and scarf, but on his way out the door, he turned back. "Have fun tonight," he called to Darcy.

She stared after him, openmouthed. He must have guessed she had a date. What was he, some kind of mind reader? Had he guessed *who* she was going out with, as well? Darcy wouldn't be at all surprised if he had. It was really weird! Scott was completely wrong about Carl. He was kind and caring and a really good friend. No way was he a wimp!

Darcy spent the rest of the afternoon getting ready for her date with Scott. It had been a long time since she'd had uninterrupted hours to devote to herself, and she enjoyed them.

First she took a long, leisurely bubble bath and read *Wuthering Heights*. The book had been assigned by Darcy's English teacher, and she had adored it from the very first page. Heathcliff reminded her of Scott in many ways, and she saw herself as his beloved Cathy.

She read until the water began to cool off. Then she put the book aside to wash her hair. Finally she was driven out of the bathroom by Caro's insistent complaints about how long she was taking. An idea for a new song formed in her mind. It would be about a love like Heathcliff's for Cathy, a love that endured forever. She toweled herself dry in a hurry and dashed straight to her desk to scribble down the words that had come to her.

She'd work on it later. Right then, however, her hair had to be dried and set, and she needed a manicure. She'd use the pearly new polish she'd bought the other day—on her toes, too, even though nobody would see them.

At supper that night Darcy could hardly swallow a bite.

"You're not getting sick, are you, dear?" her mother asked anxiously. "Are you sure you should go out tonight?"

"I'm just not hungry, Mom," said Darcy. "But I'm feeling fine. Really. Scott and I will probably get something to eat after the movie."

"Scott?" asked her father.

"Yeah," Darcy responded casually. "He's taking me to see *The Return of the Vampire*."

"You're kidding!" cried Caro. "You mean

this date is with Scott? He finally asked you for a real date?"

"No, it's a fake date," Darcy said sarcastically.

Caro ignored her comment. "He must've thought Vixen sounded pretty good yesterday," she said. "I bet he wants to get you back into Jupiter."

"Did it ever occur to you he might just want to see *me*?" Darcy retorted, annoyed. "Does he have to have an ulterior motive?" She had conveniently forgotten for the moment that sometimes she hoped that very thing.

"Girls, don't squabble," said Mrs. Bennett calmly, and Mr. Bennett added, "Don't be late, Darcy. Twelve o'clock curfew, remember? Though why you want to go out with a boy who kicked you out of his band is beyond me."

"Daddy, that was *professional*. This is personal. It's an entirely different thing. I'll be home by twelve, I promise."

Scott arrived promptly at seven-thirty, much to Darcy's relief. She had half expected him to be late, or even worse, to cancel at the last moment. She'd never seen him look so handsome. He was wearing black jeans and a new snug-fitting jacket that completely took her breath away.

Scott had borrowed his father's car for the evening, and he and Darcy met the rest of their friends in front of the Austin Theater. Pete was there with a girl Darcy didn't know, and Jupiter's new rhythm guitarist, a slight, dark-haired boy named Charlie, came with his date, Paula, a senior whom Darcy knew by sight. Tommy, Jupiter's drummer, had other plans so he couldn't make it, Pete told her.

It was wonderful being with the Jupiter guys again, Darcy thought as they took their seats in the theater. Only this time it was different, not just because she was no longer part of the band but because for the first time she was with them as Scott's girlfriend— at least for the evening. Before the lights went down, Darcy was pleased to see a lot of kids from Kennedy, many of them Jupiter groupies, and every one of the girls was looking at her with unconcealed envy. Darcy couldn't remember ever being happier or more proud. She also knew she was looking her best—shiny hair, polished nails. Chanel N° 5 and all.

The movie wasn't all that great. Darcy didn't really care for horror films, a fact she hadn't felt necessary to tell Scott. She closed her eyes during the gory parts, which amused Scott when he finally noticed it, and caused him to put his arm around her shoulders, giving her a tight hug.

I'm dreaming, she thought ecstatically, snuggling next to him. *This can't be happening!*

When the picture was over, she wasn't even sure how it had ended. Having Scott's arm around her was the only thing that stuck in her mind.

She didn't really come out of her daze until she and Scott and the rest of the kids were seated amid the noise of Dino's Pizza Shack, where the conversation was devoted exclusively to Jupiter's success.

"We're going to Philadelphia next week to cut a demo tape," Scott told her. "We know a guy who has connections with the big record companies, and he's going to peddle it for us. That's where the real money is—in records."

"Hey," Charlie cut in, "by this time next year, we might be playing Madison Square Garden!"

"Dream on," said Pete with a wry smile. "That'll be the day!"

Darcy listened, dazzled. To hear Scott talk, it all sounded possible, in spite of Pete's reservations. The other girls seemed as impressed as she was, but neither of them said very much. They appeared to be content to bask in the reflected glory of the band. *Glorified groupies*, Darcy suddenly thought. Was that what being Scott's girlfriend really meant? Becoming a supergroupie? Nobody mentioned Vixen; nobody was in the least bit interested in a struggling new band. When Darcy tried to bring Vixen into the conversation, the subject was immediately changed to Jupiter.

To her surprise Darcy grew bored. Her attention strayed back to Vixen and the next rehearsal and the new lyrics that had come to her that afternoon. She was relieved when Scott stood up and said, "OK, guys, I've got to get Darcy back home."

Maybe when they were alone together, he'd talk to her about something other than Jupiter. Even if he didn't, just to be alone with him would be wonderful. As they walked down the street to the car, Darcy saw a couple across the street who looked very much like Carl and Beth. But when the boy turned his head, she realized he was a stranger. She felt oddly relieved.

Scott didn't have much to say on the drive back to Darcy's house, so Darcy filled in the silences by telling him about Vixen's rehearsals. Scott listened and nodded and made occasional comments, although he didn't seem very interested. But when they pulled up in front of her house, Scott, leaning on the steering wheel, turned to her and said, "Hey, Darcy, I'm really glad to hear Vixen's shaping up. I wish you all the success in the world. Honestly."

"Thanks, Scott," Darcy murmured, a little surprised. "I really had a good time tonight."

"Me, too." Without another word, Scott reached over and drew her into his arms. His lips pressed hers, and Darcy melted against him. Shaken, she pulled back after several seconds, her eyes wide and starry. Her very first kiss! And it was Scott who had kissed her! She didn't know if she'd be able to summon the strength to open the car door and walk up the path.

"I'll call you, OK?" asked Scott, touching her cheek with one finger.

"Sure. OK." Darcy said shakily and trembled. She fumbled for the car door handle. When she finally found it, she let in a blast of icy air. As she wobbled up the path, she heard Scott rev the motor, and a moment later he was gone. When would he call her? she wondered, pawing through her bag to find her key. Tomorrow? The next day? *Oh, Scott,* she thought dreamily as she let herself into the house, *if you only knew how much I love you!*

Even though it was eleven-thirty and Miranda was sure to be asleep, Darcy couldn't resist the urge to call and tell her about her evening. Miranda picked up the phone on the third ring, her voice furry and half-awake. "Whazzup?" she mumbled.

"It's me, Darcy! Scott just brought me home!" she said, bubbling. "It was fantastic, Miranda! You should have seen all those girls turning green with envy when we walked into the theater! And afterward we went to Dino's—"

"Do you know what time it is?" Miranda

moaned. "What are you, crazy or something? Can't you wait and tell me tomorrow? I'm coming to practice."

"I know, but I had to tell you this—he *kissed* me! Scott Maguire *kissed* me! I can hardly believe it!"

"If I tell you *I* believe it, will you let me go back to sleep?" pleaded Miranda.

"Some friend you are!" Darcy sighed. "I thought you'd be happy for me."

"I'm very happy for you. I'm so happy, I'll probably dream happy dreams for what's left of the night, if you'll just go away!"

"Good night, Miranda, dear," said Darcy, hanging up. Not even Miranda's drowsiness could spoil her lovely mood. What did Miranda know, anyway? She'd never been in love, not the way Darcy was with Scott—the way Cathy was with Heathcliff. How could she possibly understand?

Darcy's rosy glow carried her through the next day, giving her added energy to rehearse the group extra hard. She did keep one ear cocked for the phone throughout the rehearsal. Even when Scott hadn't called by the time practice was over, she wasn't terribly upset.

He'd probably had practice, too. He'd call her that evening. She could wait until then.

It turned out that Carl hadn't driven to her house that day. His van had transmission trouble, so he was unable to take the girls home as usual. A boy came by to pick up Beth, and Lori and Miranda left together, so Darcy had no opportunity to fill Miranda in on the details of her date with Scott. Carl stayed after the others had left, tinkering with Lori's amp, and for the first time Darcy found herself alone with him.

"Thanks for taking a look at that," she said.

Carl grinned. "I wish I knew as much about cars as I do about this. I'll have to take the van to the shop tomorrow. It'll probably cost me a lot, too,"

Darcy suddenly felt guilty. "I guess it would have helped if we were being paid for our performance at the Community House," she ventured.

"Sure, it would have helped, but it's an investment in the future, like you said. Once people have heard us perform, we'll get plenty of other work that pays. And in the meantime, we're having fun, right?"

"Right," Darcy agreed. Carl was so different from Scott, she thought. She hadn't dared tell Scott that Vixen's first performance was going to be for free—he'd have said she was crazy. Success was important to Scott, and success meant money in part. Well, Darcy had to admit she agreed with him, but she had her own way of going about it.

Having gotten the amp back in working order, Carl stood up. He was tall, as tall as Scott. "What other kinds of music do you like, Darcy?" he asked, tucking a screwdriver into his hip pocket. "Do you like classical? The orchestra's doing three of Bach's *Brandenburg* Concertos at their next concert."

"Oh, I love Bach," Darcy said excitedly. "I'm working on the Fugue in A Minor for my piano teacher now."

"Would you play it for me?" Carl asked.

"Sure. Let's go upstairs to the real piano, though. Hey, you've never been upstairs, have you?" She paused, suddenly shy.

"I'd really like to hear it. Unless you'd rather not play," he added. "My oldest sister, Joanna, plays the piano, and my parents were always making her play when they had company. She hated it."

"You're not a guest." Darcy laughed. "Come on. But you have to promise not to cringe when I hit a wrong note!"

"I promise," said Carl solemnly.

But when Darcy was seated at the piano and Carl had sat down on the sofa in the living room, she felt a moment of panic. None of her other friends, not even Miranda, had ever asked to hear her play. Performing at the annual recital was one thing, but playing for just one person was something else. Her fingers felt stiff and awkward, and she wished she'd spent more time working on Bach and maybe a little less on the Beatles.

Carl leaned over and picked up a copy of the *National Geographic* from the coffee table. Leafing through the magazine, he said, "Just pretend I'm not here."

Darcy breathed a sigh of relief. "OK. You read, and I'll play."

She made a few false starts, but then the music took over, clean and precise as a mathematical equation, and her fingers seemed to have a life of their own, hitting the keys with an authority that even to her own critical ears sounded fairly good. When she had finished, Carl looked up from his magazine and nodded. "That was great, Darcy."

Darcy blushed. "Thanks. And thank you for not looking at me!"

"Oh, I was looking at you, all right. You just didn't notice. You were so wrapped up in the music, you wouldn't have noticed if a satellite crashed through the roof."

"I think I *might* have lost my place, if that had happened," said Darcy, laughing.

She played some popular selections then, some Billy Joel and Elton John and a few old Beatles numbers. When her mother came in from the meeting she'd attended, Darcy introduced her to Carl, then Caro burst in, full of news about her friend Betsy starting a group of her own. Caro had decided she wanted to take guitar lessons so that she could join the group. Carl gave her the name and phone number of a friend who taught guitar, and Caro dashed off to make the call.

It was after six when Carl finally left, and as he did, Mrs. Bennett said, "What a nice boy, Darcy. Aren't you lucky he auditioned for your band!"

"Yeah, I guess I am," Darcy agreed.

But she couldn't help thinking about Scott—he hadn't called as he'd promised. Oh, well. Maybe he was still rehearsing. Maybe he'd call after supper.

Chapter Seven

Scott didn't call after supper, though, or the next day, or the day after that. Darcy made up every excuse she could think of for him: Jupiter was so busy practicing, getting ready to cut their demo tape; the Bennetts' line was busy—Caro was on the phone a lot with Betsy these days; he'd lost her phone number; his phone was out of order; *her* phone was out of order. The one reason she didn't want to think about was the one she was increasingly afraid was true—he'd simply forgotten. He probably told girls he'd call them all the time. Scott knew so many girls. . . .

"Listen, Darcy, stop eating your heart out," Miranda advised on Wednesday as Darcy moped along the halls of Kennedy on her way to the biology lab. "That's just the way Scott is. You ought to know that by now."

"You're a real comfort, you know that?" Darcy said irritably. "And I'm not eating my heart out. I'm just disappointed." But *disappointed* was a very mild word for the misery she felt.

Suddenly Miranda poked her sharply in the ribs. "Hey, here he comes. Maybe he'll tell you why he hasn't called."

Darcy looked up. Sure enough, there was Scott, in earnest conversation with a petite, dark-haired girl, who was gazing at him adoringly. As he was about to pass Darcy and Miranda, he paused and smiled. "Hey, Darce, how's it going?" he asked cheerfully.

"Hi, Scott. OK, I guess. I haven't seen you around much lately." *Or heard anything from you, either,* she thought.

"We're cutting that tape tomorrow night," he told her. "This guy who set it up thinks maybe Starburst Records will be interested. Keep your fingers crossed!"

"Yeah, sure," Darcy mumbled, a cold anger beginning to replace her sorrow. "Good luck," she added as he and the girl continued down the hall. It was obvious he didn't care about her one bit, Darcy thought angrily. He probably kissed every girl he dated. Well, if he didn't care, neither did she. Ignoring Miranda's sympathetic glance, she headed for the door of the lab. She'd been an idiot, that was all. Her head had been in the clouds, but it wouldn't be anymore. Vixen's performance at the Community House was only ten days away. If her personal life was a disaster, she'd concentrate on her professional life and the success of Vixen. She'd lost sight of her goal, and that was a big mistake. Even if Scott wasn't interested in her as a girl, he'd have to sit up and take notice of Vixen's triumph. And it *would* be a triumph, Darcy vowed grimly.

"No way! Forget it!" Carl was adamant. "I am not going to wear sequins and Lycra. Absolutely not!"

The group was discussing stage clothes for their first performance, and Darcy had just brought up her idea for Vixen's image.

"I'm not exactly the sequin type, either," Lori agreed. "I mean, I don't exactly have a great body. It's a big body, but it's not, well, sexy, you know?"

"I'd *love* sequins," said Beth. "But I see the problem. We ought to have a unified look, and it has to be a look that suits all of us. Darcy and I could get away with some glamour, but—"

In response to Lori's scowl, she quickly added, "Not that you're not attractive, Lori. You're a knockout, but you have a style of your own, and it's definitely not glitter. As for Carl, I have to agree with him. It just wouldn't work."

"Beth's right," Miranda said briskly. "Unified is the word. Most other groups wear whatever they feel like at the moment. The last time I went to a Hit and Run concert, the bass player was wearing a T-shirt with the sleeves cut off and grungy jeans, and the other guys, well, forget it!"

"Hey, I'm hidden behind my drums, anyway. I could wear pajamas for all anybody would care." Carl laughed, his good humor restored.

"But we definitely need an image," Darcy persisted. "We're new, and we're good, and we want people to remember us. How about a sequined headband?" she asked Carl hopefully. "It would keep the hair out of your eyes."

"No way," repeated Carl, and she could tell he meant it. "Maybe a bandanna, but no glitz. You girls do what you want, but don't dress me up like a prize poodle!"

Darcy sighed. So much for her dream of standing in the spotlight, sparkling like a Christmas tree. "OK, sequins are out." She thought a moment. "Carl mentioned bandannas. What if we all wore jeans—*good* jeans that fit—and colored T-shirts, and tied bandannas around our necks and foreheads? Those bright-colored ones you can get at the dime store for about a dollar each?"

"Great!" said Miranda enthusiastically. "That won't be expensive, and it'll be uniform."

"I can get a whole bunch of them at Woolworth's," Lori volunteered. "I even get a discount. I'd feel a lot more comfortable wearing stuff like that."

It wasn't the way Darcy had envisioned her band, but she gave in. Carl flashed her a grateful glance when she agreed, and that made her feel better about it. Besides, if the band sounded good, it wouldn't really matter what they wore, and if they were lousy, all the fancy costumes in the world wouldn't make any difference.

Lori was meeting a friend after practice, and still another boy came by to take Beth home, so Carl and Miranda hung around for a while with Darcy, listening to records and talking about the upcoming performance. Before Darcy knew it, it was six o'clock, and Mrs. Bennett invited Carl and Miranda to stay for supper.

It was the first time Carl had met Darcy's father, and they got along instantly. It turned out that they were both Philadelphia Eagles fans, so everybody talked football for most of the meal. When Carl and Miranda finally left in Carl's van, which was in working order again, Darcy realized that for the first time in days, she'd actually spent several hours without once thinking about Scott Maguire.

One week later on Saturday night, Darcy stood in front of the mirror in the women's room of the Community House, staring at her reflection with unseeing eyes. For the first time in her life, she was a helpless victim of stage fright; she was shaking all over. Vixen was scheduled to go on in fifteen minutes, and her mind was a complete blank. She'd have to step out into the spotlight, microphone in hand, and she couldn't remember one word of any of the songs they'd rehearsed over and over again, not even "Lovesick Girl." The Community House was packed with kids, all of them gathered to pass judgment on the new band. If Vixen bombed, Darcy would never be able to show her face again!

Miranda came out of one of the stalls, washed her hands at the sink, then tapped Darcy on the shoulder. "You ready to go?"

Darcy jumped, dropping her comb. "No! No, I'm not ready. I'll never be ready." She moaned. "I think I'm going to be sick."

"No, you're not. You look fantastic. Except maybe you ought to put on some more blusher. You look a little pale."

Darcy stood numbly, letting Miranda rub some color into her cheeks. Then Miranda retrieved her comb from the sink and tucked it into Darcy's hip pocket. "OK. You're all set. Vixen's going to be a smash. There's absolutely nothing to worry about. Come on, let's go."

Darcy allowed herself to be led out of the bathroom, but each foot felt as though it was weighted with lead. She'd never felt that way in all her life, not at her piano recitals, not when she'd performed with Jupiter. She'd never done a lead vocal in public. What if her voice cracked? What if she couldn't make a sound?

"Is Scott here?" she asked, clinging to Miranda's hand.

"I haven't seen him," Miranda told her calmly. "But he'll turn up, you can count on that."

Darcy nodded. She and Miranda joined the other members of the band. None of them looked half as nervous as she felt. Lori and Beth were joking and laughing with some friends, and Carl was adjusting the lights he'd set up. Miranda shoved a can of soda into Darcy's shaking hand, whispering, "Everything's going to be fine. Vixen'll knock 'em dead. Really."

Carl finished talking to Billy, a friend of his who had volunteered to act as Vixen's technician. He was wearing a blue bandanna headband and had tied a yellow one around his neck. Smiling down at her, he rested a hand on her shoulder. It felt warm and comforting.

"How are you doing?" he asked.

"OK, I guess." But she was trembling, and he felt it.

"Hey, remember what we agreed? This is supposed to be fun. We've got our act together. Now all we have to do is let the rest of them enjoy it. We've got it made." He slipped his arm around her shoulders and hugged her briefly. Darcy felt much better. A shiver of excitement ran through her.

"You're right." She took a deep breath, which steadied her nerves. "I'm ready whenever the rest of you are."

"Great! Let's do it!"

Carl signaled to Lori and Beth, who immediately picked up their instruments and began tuning. Moments later, the lights dimmed, and a spotlight picked up Charlie Bellows, a Community House member who was in charge of the dance. "Your attention, please!" he shouted into the microphone, and the din began to subside. "For the first time on any stage, the Community House is proud to present—*Vixen!*"

There was a roar of cheers and some scattered applause, and the spotlight switched to Darcy. Dazzled by its brilliance, she hesitated a second, then stepped forward and seized the mike.

"Hi, everybody!" she cried, her voice breaking just a little. "We're Vixen, and we're gonna rock 'n' roll!"

She gave the downbeat, and the band began their version of Pat Benatar's "Treat Me Right." Darcy hit the keys of her piano, and Beth belted out the lyrics. She sang all their Pat Benatar numbers. Darcy thought she sounded just like her. The music pounded out through their amps, filling the huge room. It was like their rehearsals, only better, bigger, and more exciting. Darcy's stage fright melted away. Carl had been right, as usual. It was fun! She'd never had so much fun!

When the first set was over, all the members of Vixen were dripping with sweat, dying of thirst, and high on excitement. The screams and applause of the audience rang in Darcy's ears. They were a hit! She was engulfed in a tangle of arms as Carl, Miranda, Beth, and Lori all hugged Darcy and one another. They could hardly wait to begin the next set.

By the end of the evening, Vixen's success was assured. "Lovesick Girl" had been received with as much enthusiasm as the copy numbers. Eager kids crowded around the members of the band, shouting congratulations. Darcy noticed that some of the Jupiter groupies were hanging on to Carl, just the way they usually attacked Scott. They'd discovered that Jupiter hadn't cornered the market on attractive guys. And the girls were surrounded by boys who were apparently in the process of becoming Vixen groupies.

Caro and three of her friends forced their way through the crowd. Darcy was almost knocked off her feet by her sister's impetuous hug.

"You were terrific, Darcy!" Caro cried. "And would you believe Mom and Daddy were here? They didn't want to tell you they were coming in case it would make you nervous. You should have heard them telling all the chaperons that you're their daughter!"

"Hey, Darcy, don't forget there's a party at my house," Lori called to her. "You know where I live, right?"

"Yeah, sure," Darcy called back, grinning. Her eyes roamed the crowd. In spite of her annoyance at Scott, she couldn't help hoping he'd been there to see what a success her first performance had been. Somehow it didn't mean as much without him.

Suddenly she felt an arm slip around her waist. Startled, she looked up to find that the arm belonged to Scott. He was grinning at her, dark eyes glowing. He bent over and kissed her on the cheek.

Darcy blushed, and her heart beat faster. "Long time no see," she said coolly.

"Congratulations," he said, pressing her close to him. "Fantastic gig. No joke."

"Thanks." Darcy smiled, all her annoyance fading away. "I was wondering if you'd come."

"How could I stay away? I taught you everything you know, remember?"

"Not *everything*," Darcy objected, looking around to see who Scott's date was. A lot of girls were eyeing him, but none appeared to be his date.

"You're coming with me," Scott commanded, drawing her away from the others. "We'll go to the Isle of Capri for something to eat."

"But—" Darcy protested, "I have to help pack up all our stuff. And then I'm supposed to be going to Lori's party."

"So tell your friends you'll see them later. They can break down without you. I want to talk to you."

It was as though she had been hypnotized. Darcy made a feeble excuse to Lori, telling her she'd come to the party later. Lori raised her eyebrows, glanced at Scott, but didn't object. As she put on her jacket, Darcy met Carl's blue eyes. His expression was impossible to interpret. For some reason she felt she owed him an explanation, but there wasn't time. A few minutes later, she found herself on Dartmouth Street, her arm linked in Scott's, heading for his father's car.

Seated across from Scott in the wood-paneled dimness of the Isle of Capri, sipping the Coke she had ordered, Darcy tried to pull herself together. She would have been content just to sit there in a happy daze forever, savoring the memory of Vixen's success, but she knew she had to say something. "What did you want to talk to me about?" she asked.

For the second time since she'd known him, Scott seemed at a loss for words. The first time, Darcy recalled, had been when he'd told her she was fired from Jupiter. But this time it couldn't be bad news. Maybe he was getting up the courage to tell her what she'd longed to hear—that he realized she was the girl for him. Darcy held her breath.

"Well—" he began, then paused. "There's a rumor going around that you're going to enter Vixen in the Battle of the Bands. Is that true?"

That certainly wasn't what Darcy expected. "I meant to all along. Now that we've shown what we can do, I definitely will," she said.

"If you do, you'll be creamed, you know that?"

Darcy blinked, surprised at his bluntness. "What makes you say that? I think Vixen has as good a chance as any other band."

Scott leaned across the tiny table and took Darcy's hand. "Listen, Darce, Vixen's good, but not *that* good. You'd be competing against a lot of bands that have more experience. You're just starting out—you shouldn't try to do too much. I don't want to see you get hurt."

In spite of her disappointment that romance wasn't what Scott had in mind, Darcy was touched that he seemed concerned about her feelings. She felt excited, too. If he didn't think Vixen was good enough to be a threat to Jupiter's reputation, he wouldn't be trying to talk her out of entering the Battle of the Bands, which made her even more determined to do it. On the other hand, she'd be placing herself in direct competition with Scott, which wouldn't exactly be great for their relationship, whatever that was.

"I don't know," she said, hedging. "You may be right. But my band has worked very hard. I kind of owe it to us to enter."

"Well, it's your decision. You're the boss. I just wouldn't want to see you—"

"Make a fool of myself?" Darcy suggested sharply, attempting to draw her hand away. But Scott raised her fingers to his lips, kissing them lightly, and Darcy felt herself weaken.

"That's not what I was going to say," he said, his brown eyes serious. "It's just like I said, I don't want to see you get hurt, that's all."

Darcy managed a faint laugh. "I'm tougher than I look," she told him. "Don't worry about me."

"But you'll think about what I've been telling you, won't you?" he asked, holding her hand against his cheek. "I really care about you, Darcy. You know that."

Did she? Darcy wanted so much to believe him. . . . "I'll think about it. I promise," she whispered.

"That's my girl!" He seemed satisfied and kissed her fingers lightly again.

Just then the waitress arrived with their order. "Hey, if you're supposed to be going to some victory party," Scott said, looking at his watch, "we'd better eat fast."

"OK," Darcy said.

After they finished eating, Scott paid the check, then helped Darcy on with her jacket, and they walked arm in arm back to the car.

When they reached Lori's house, she turned to him. "You want to come in?" she asked. "I'm sure Lori wouldn't mind."

"No, that's OK. This is your night."

As Darcy made a move to open the car door, she felt Scott's hand on her shoulder, drawing her close to him. She lifted her face to his, and their lips met in a long, lingering kiss.

"Congratulations," he said when he finally released her. "Have fun at your party. We'll keep in touch, OK?"

"Yes, thanks. OK," Darcy murmured shakily. "See you."

"You'd better believe it," Scott replied and grinned. He was already gunning the motor as she got out, and as soon as her feet touched the curb, he pulled away, tires spinning on the ice.

Chapter Eight

As Darcy entered Lori's house, she was greeted by the sound of her own voice belting out "Lovesick Girl" at top volume. She stood there, gaping, taken aback, but before she could react, Lori grabbed her by the arm and dragged her inside, hollering over the music, "I thought you would never come! Billy taped the whole performance. Come on in and listen. It's terrific!"

Darcy took off her down jacket, tossed it on a bench, and let herself be pulled into the living room, where she found all of Vixen plus what looked like half of Kennedy High sprawled on the furniture and the floor, listening to the music. Miranda seized her hand

and pulled her down beside her where she was sitting on the floor next to Billy. Her face was flushed, her hair seemed to be standing on end, and her eyes were shining.

"You guys really sound super! What kept you? Everybody's been asking where you were."

"What did you tell them?" Darcy asked.

"What do you *think* I told them? That you went out with Scott. Why? Was it a secret?"

"No, no. That's OK," said Darcy absently, her mind on the music. *Is that really me?* she wondered, awestruck. *Gosh, I'm better than I thought!*

"Wait till the tape's over. I have fabulous news," whispered Miranda. Darcy nodded. Looking around the room, she saw Carl, sitting with Beth cozily perched on his knee. His eyes met hers, and he raised one hand in a friendly salute. Darcy grinned back, still dazed by the sound of Vixen. They'd taped rehearsals from time to time, but they'd never sounded like this. *Billy must have super equipment*, she thought. *Or did we really play that well?*

When the number ended, she could hardly keep from applauding with the others—not for herself, but for the band as a whole. The next song began, and now it was Beth's voice that filled the room. Somebody thrust an ice cold soda into her hand, and Darcy accepted it numbly. It was weird, hearing the performance on tape, almost as though it were another group entirely.

"So here's my news," Miranda was saying, bending her head close to Darcy's. "Right after the first set, Jody West came up to me and practically *begged* me to line up Vixen for her Sweet Sixteen next Saturday—she had had someone lined up, and they canceled, and she's been frantically looking for a replacement. Then Mr. Bellamy from the Community House told me they want us for their St. Patrick's Day dance the next Saturday! And then the president of the youth group from Saint Luke's Church said they're planning a dance in April, and he wants Vixen to play. And they're all going to *pay*! What do you think of that?"

Still dazed, Darcy nodded. "Great. Really fantastic! I can't believe it's all happening!"

"It's happening, all right," Billy put in,

leaning close to Miranda. "And I told Miranda I want to be your number-one roadie for all future performances. I have a couple of friends who'd like to help out, too. There's a guy I know who's really into lighting effects. He wants to light your next show. He has his own equipment, so it won't cost you anything. Vixen's dynamite, Darcy!"

"Thanks, Billy. And thanks for recording the performance. I just can't *believe* it!" she repeated faintly.

Again she glanced over at Carl. Beth bounced up and down on his knee in time to the music, and another girl was bending over him, whispering in his ear. He seemed to have forgotten Darcy completely. Suddenly Darcy felt annoyed, though she knew she had no reason to be. Still, he might have made an effort to come over to her, talk to her a little, share their triumph.

"I'm starving," she announced, scrambling to her feet. "Point me to the food!"

Several of her friends from school immediately materialized, leading her to the Berkowitzes' dining room, where a few remaining slices of pizza were cooling in their boxes. Darcy chose a piece with pepperoni heaped on it and sank her teeth into it while she listened to the kids praise her and Vixen. If the pizza was cold, the words were warm, and to Darcy nothing had ever tasted better.

She'd just finished eating when she became aware of Carl standing next to her, hands in his hip pockets, a smile on his face. "So Vixen's a big success, just the way you planned," he said.

Darcy smiled back. "The way I'd *hoped*," she corrected. "You were all wonderful. You made it all happen!"

"What did the great Scott Maguire have to say?" he persisted. "Did you tell him we're entering the Battle of the Bands?"

Darcy looked away. "Oh, he thought we were fine. As for the Battle of the Bands, well . . ."

"Well, what?" Carl was still smiling, but his eyes were watchful.

"I mentioned it, that is, *he* mentioned it, but he's not sure—"

"He doesn't think we're ready for the 'big time,' is that it?"

Darcy turned her attention to a platter of cookies. How did Carl always know things about people? It was spooky sometimes. She selected a chocolate-chip cookie and took a bite. "He said he thought we'd be creamed by the other bands," she told him bluntly. "He said we won't have had enough experience by April to compete with groups that have been performing longer."

"Do you think he's right?" Carl asked, his eyes never leaving her face. "Let me put it another way. Did he make you feel he was right?"

"Well, not exactly."

"We're ready, Darcy, or we will be when the time comes. You know it, and I know it, and Beth and Lori know it, too. And so does Scott. I think that's why he's trying to convince you we're *not* ready. Jupiter doesn't exactly welcome competition, from what I've heard."

"Jupiter doesn't have to be afraid of anybody!" Darcy cried, turning on him. "Jupiter's the best there is!"

"I think Vixen's the best there is, now," Carl said quietly. "And you ought to think so, too, as the leader of the pack."

"I *do* think so!" Darcy retorted hotly. "I told Scott that I'd think about it. And I will. There's nothing I wouldn't do for Vixen."

"Except compete with Scott," Carl said softly, and Darcy felt her face grow hot.

"Scott has nothing to do with it," she snapped, but the fact that she wasn't being completely honest with Carl upset her. "What I mean is," she explained, "maybe we're *not* quite ready to enter into competition with Jupiter and the other bands that have been around for a while. April's only a month away."

Carl shook his head. "That doesn't sound like you, Darcy. You've always been the one who kept pushing us to go that extra mile, rehearsing day after day, telling us how important it was for Vixen to succeed. Now that we're on our way, you've changed your mind."

"I have not!" Darcy cried. "Maybe we're not quite ready now, but by April we will be!"

"You bet we will!" said Carl, his blue eyes flashing approval. "So you're going to enter Vixen in the Battle of the Bands, right?"

"Right!" said Darcy. Somebody grabbed her from behind, squeezing her hard around the middle, and she gasped. It was Lori, Beth at her side, and both of them were beaming.

"Jupiter, eat your heart out!" cried Beth,

bouncing up and down. "Get ready to make room for Vixen!"

"Yeah!" shouted Lori, and the four of them hugged each other, laughing. Miranda and Billy joined them then, and Miranda began telling the others about the work she'd lined up for them. Darcy was caught up in the general excitement. Scott would understand, she felt sure. If he really cared about her, as he'd said he did, he'd be proud of her. They were equals now. She was a person in her own right. Of course he'd understand.

An hour later, when most of Lori's guests had bundled themselves into their jackets and said goodbye, Carl seized Darcy's hand. "Hey, want a ride home?" he asked. "It's just about one o'clock, and it's snowing like crazy."

"It is?" Darcy ran to look out the window. Sure enough, snow was swirling down, all but obliterating the streetlight outside. Everything looked so pretty.

"If this keeps up, maybe school will be closed on Monday," Lori suggested happily. "It looks like a real blizzard!"

"I'd better be getting *you* home, too," said Billy, who had his arm around Miranda. Darcy, had never seen her look so happy. She was nestling close to Billy, and for the first time in weeks, she wasn't clutching her clipboard. *Well!* thought Darcy, amused. She'd have to get the details the next day.

Billy helped Miranda into her coat, and Carl found Darcy's jacket on the bench and helped her into it. After he'd retrieved his own jacket and wrapped a scarf around his neck, they said goodbye to Lori and thanked her for the great party. Beth had left some time before, after giving Carl a big kiss.

A moment later, Darcy and Carl were outside, fighting to keep the blinding snow out of their faces.

"Where's your car?" Darcy asked, clutching Carl's arm as they cautiously maneuvered the steps down to the sidewalk.

"I think that's it," he said, gesturing toward a white mound beside the curb. It must have been snowing for quite a while.

"It's so beautiful!" Darcy said as they struggled in the direction of the white-shrouded shape.

"Shucks, ma'am, it's just a plain ol' ordinary car," said Carl, joking.

"Not the car, dummy, the *snow*!" Darcy

giggled. She paused, appreciating the silence. "Boy, it's a good thing the snow didn't start before the dance! We'd have played to an empty house."

"Watch your step. It's slippery," Carl warned, and Darcy clung more tightly to his arm as her feet started to slide out from under her.

At last they were snug inside Carl's father's battered station wagon, which grudgingly, after a few whines and moans and turns of the ignition key, sprang to life. As Carl drove down the deserted streets, Darcy relaxed next to him, smiling contentedly. It was as though the two of them were enclosed in their own private, snowy world. She was almost sorry when the car rolled gently to a stop in front of her house.

"It looks like good packing snow," she said as the windshield wipers labored to clear the glass. "My sister and I used to build fantastic snowmen in weather like this, only there were some nasty kids down the block who always knocked their heads off."

"I used to be a nasty little kid," said Carl, grinning, "and I used to knock down snowmen, too, but that was in Philadelphia. You can't pin it on me!"

They both laughed, then Carl asked, "Do you ski?"

"Me? No way! I'm about as athletic as—as a tree." Darcy laughed. "I'd probably break every bone in my body if I tried to go down one of those scary hills."

"How about cross-country? That's when you just glide along the trails. It's easy."

"I don't know—" said Darcy, shivering.

"It's fun," Carl persisted. "And it's not hard to learn. Want to give it a try tomorrow? My sisters left some of their skis when they went away to college. You could use Ellen's. I'll teach you how. We could ski all over town, up and down the streets and in the park. Not even *you* could get hurt doing that, I promise."

Darcy was tempted, but still she hesitated. "I might break the skis or something. I'm really a klutz."

"Come on! You'll love it. I could come by about one o'clock. I'm a pretty good teacher, if I do say so myself. What about it?"

"Well—" A thought struck Darcy. "What about Beth?" she asked.

"What *about* Beth?" Carl repeated.

"Wouldn't you rather be doing something with her? You two seemed to be, you know, kind of—" she floundered, remembering Beth's sitting on Carl's lap and later, their kissing.

Carl laughed, his white teeth shining in the moonlight. "No, I don't know," he said, reaching out and taking her hand. "I mean, I know what you're thinking, but it's not true. I like Beth, sure, but only as a friend. I don't feel about her the way I do about—" He broke off, obviously embarrassed, then quickly changed the subject. "What about you? You and Scott? If you have a date or something—"

"Oh, no, nothing like that!" Darcy quickly assured him. "Look, I really do have to go. My parents'll be climbing the walls."

"So do you want to try cross-country skiing with me tomorrow?" Carl was still holding her hand, and Darcy squeezed his briefly.

"Yeah, sure. But if it's a total disaster, don't say I didn't warn you!"

"It couldn't be a total disaster, not with you," said Carl softly.

Darcy realized with a funny little thrill that if she didn't get out of the car right away, he was going to kiss her. She didn't know how she knew it, but she did. Her free hand was on the door latch, but she didn't push it down.

And sure enough, Carl leaned over and kissed her gently on the lips. It was a very nice kiss. Savoring it, she whispered, "See you tomorrow. I mean, today!"

She fumbled with the door, and Carl immediately opened the one on his side and came around, tugging at the frozen handle until hers opened. Gripping her firmly by the elbow, he guided her up the path until she was safely on her front porch. He waited while she found her key and inserted it in the lock.

"Good night, Carl. Thanks for bringing me home," she murmured, feeling strangely shy.

"My pleasure," he said, touching one hand to his snow-covered head in a brief salute. Then he turned to make his way cautiously down the icy steps. On the bottom one his feet slid out from under him, and he landed on his back on the path. Before Darcy could do more than clap a hand to her mouth and gasp, he was up again, laughing and dusting himself off. "Talk about klutzes!" he called, waving to her through the swirling snow. A moment later he was lost to her view, but she waited on the steps until she heard the thunk of the car door closing and the engine of the station wagon catching hold.

"Cross-country skiing?" she muttered. "I've got to be out of my mind!"

She stamped her feet to get the snow off, then unlocked the door and went inside. She caught sight of the note her parents had left, tucked under the lamp on the desk. "We know you're at Lori's, but please wake us up when you come in," she read. Smiling, she went up the stairs to her parents' bedroom.

But I'm not going to tell them I've been kissed by two boys in one night! she thought. They wouldn't know how to handle that. And neither, Darcy realized, did she.

Chapter Nine

Darcy woke up to find her room ablaze with dazzling sunshine, reflected from the snow outside. She'd forgotten to pull the blinds when she had gone to bed, and the glare actually hurt her eyes.

She squinted at the clock on her bedside table—eleven forty-five! She'd never slept so late. Darcy stretched luxuriously, enjoying the unaccustomed sensation of having an entire unscheduled day ahead of her. Suddenly she remembered she'd promised to go cross-country skiing with Carl. But that wasn't like having to practice—that was pure fun! She snuggled down under the blankets, thinking about the previous night. It had been a triumph, no doubt about it: the sensation the band had made; going to the Isle of Capri with Scott; his kissing her; going to Lori's party; Carl's taking her home; and his kissing her. . . .

What a night! thought Darcy. All of a sudden life was more complicated and much more interesting than she'd ever dreamed it could be. An image of Miranda snuggled up next to Billy popped into her head, and impulsively she leaped out of bed and made for the phone on her desk. She had to call Miranda and find out if anything exciting had happened to *her* the night before.

Miranda's voice was as bright and bouncy as if she'd been up for hours. In response to Darcy's questions, she giggled. "Hold it! Take it easy! What's all this third degree?"

"Oh, come on, Miranda! You and Billy obviously had something going at Lori's last night. I tell you everything. Don't hold out on me!"

"We-e-ell," Miranda hedged, then plunged ahead. "Billy brought me home. We like each other a lot. You wouldn't *believe* all the things we have in common, Darcy! So we're going to the movies this afternoon, and I guess we'll take it from there."

"Did he kiss you?" Darcy asked eagerly.

Silence. Then a giggle. Then, "Did Carl kiss *you*?"

"I asked you first!"

"Yes, he did! Now it's your turn. What about Carl?"

"We-e-ell, as a matter of fact, he did. And then he fell down in the snow, and we're going cross-country skiing this afternoon. Don't laugh!"

"Laugh? Who's laughing? I just fainted, that's all. Darcy Bennett, girl jock! Seriously, Darcy, Carl's really a terrific guy. I like him a lot better than—well, than you know who."

Darcy frowned. "There's absolutely no comparison, Miranda. I mean, I like them both, but they're so different."

Miranda sighed. "Are they ever! I couldn't agree with you more. It's about time you realized that the only thing Scott cares about is Scott—and Jupiter."

Darcy felt confused, and it wasn't a feeling she enjoyed. Miranda was wrong, of course. Scott had said he cared about her, and she believed him. Or she wanted to believe him, which amounted to the same thing. Still, he had tried to talk her out of the Battle of the Bands. . . .

"Listen, I have to shower and get dressed," Darcy said briskly. "Carl's coming to pick me up in a little while. I think it's great about you and Billy, I really do. Keep me posted, OK?"

"Sure," said Miranda. "Just don't fall down and break something. Vixen's playing for that Sweet Sixteen next weekend, remember."

"I could play in a wheelchair if I had to!" Darcy retorted. "See you tomorrow!"

Darcy had just finished showering and was standing in her underwear, debating whether to wear a pair of shocking pink long johns under her jeans, when the telephone rang.

If that's Miranda with more words of wisdom . . . , she thought, picking up the receiver.

"Hi, Darcy? It's Scott. How are you doing?"

"Scott! Hi!" she said breathlessly. "What's up?"

"Nothing much. Just wondering how you're feeling after the big blast last night."

"Lori's party? It was fun. I had a great time."

"Cool. Hey, I was wondering if you were doing anything this afternoon because I might come over later. I forgot to tell you last night that I've got a copy of the Jupiter cut we did in Philly. It sounds fantastic. I thought maybe you'd like to hear it."

Would I! Drat! thought Darcy. Of course she wanted to hear the tape, but she couldn't break her date with Carl. "Gee, Scott, I'm really sorry, but I'm going out. Maybe I could hear it some other time," she suggested.

"Well, how about tonight? I could come over after supper."

Darcy's heart leaped. "That'd be great! Maybe I could borrow the tape Billy made of our performance last night, and we could listen to that, too!"

"Sure, but the Jupiter tape is professional quality, you know? It's not like the kind of thing some kid makes during a gig. Wait till you hear it. You'll flip out. I know Jupiter's going to get a record contract out of this. I'll see you about seven, OK?"

"OK," Darcy whispered. She hung up the phone in a daze. Scott actually wanted to see her again!

What had she been doing when he called? Oh, yes, the long johns. Opening a bureau drawer, she rummaged around until she found them. She'd need her leg warmers, too, the striped ones, and a couple of sweaters. And she'd better call Miranda and find out how to contact Billy about the Vixen tape. Or better yet, Carl would know where he lived. Maybe they could drop by his house and pick it up.

Darcy brushed her hair until it crackled with static electricity. As she did she sang the refrain of "Lovesick Girl," changing the lyrics slightly: "She loves you from afar. You're her superstar, And you *do* know she's alive!"

It was a wonderful afternoon. Carl was, as he had promised, a good teacher, and it didn't take Darcy long at all to pick up the technique of cross-country skiing, or cross-city skiing as Carl called it. They glided through the snow-covered streets, meeting other skiers and kids of all ages, Caro among them, dragging their sleds behind them. Darcy felt like a little kid herself as she and Carl stopped from time to time to have snowball fights with their friends, laughing and shouting. A lot of older people were out, too, shoveling their sidewalks or digging out their cars, and young couples trudged along, pulling babies on sleds. There was virtually no traffic. It was as though the entire town had become one large winter carnival.

Billy didn't live too far away. They found him out front shoveling just before leaving to pick up Miranda. He got the tape for Darcy, then walked with them part of the way to Miranda's house.

When he had turned down her street, Darcy said to Carl, "I talked to Miranda this morning. She likes Billy a lot. I'm so glad. It was great to hear her sound so happy!"

Carl nodded. "Billy told me last night that he's never met a girl like Miranda—smart and pretty and not off the wall. He's sort of shy, so I'm surprised he moved in so fast!"

They both laughed, then glided along side by side toward Darcy's house.

When they'd taken off their skis, Darcy suggested that they make a snowman. "The very best snowman ever, to make up for all the ones that got their heads knocked off!"

Caro and some of her friends soon joined them, and between them they made not one snowman but four. Caro dashed into the house and came out with a collection of bandannas, which she tied around their heads and necks. "It's Vixen!" she shouted. "All we need are the instruments!"

Then Mrs. Bennett called them all inside for hot cocoa.

Caro and her friends soon went up to Caro's room, and Mr. and Mrs. Bennett went outside to take a walk, leaving Darcy and Carl alone in front of the fireplace, where Mr. Bennett had built a roaring fire. Darcy and Carl sprawled on their stomachs, stockinged feet stretched out behind them, their faces flushed from the warmth. Darcy took a sip of hot chocolate, then set the mug down beside her. She felt totally content.

"What a great day," said Carl, and Darcy nodded, smiling.

"The best," she agreed. "And I only fell down twice!"

"Three times, but who's counting?" Carl said, teasing her. "You'll discover muscles you never knew you had."

Darcy grimaced. "Thanks for warning me.

I guess I'd better soak in a hot tub before I go to bed tonight."

She rested her head on her folded arms and gazed drowsily at the dancing flames. After a few minutes, she felt Carl's hand on her back, and his strong fingers began to massage the muscles that were already beginning to tighten up. "Mmmm, that feels good," she murmured.

"It's another of my hidden talents," said Carl. "You know, it's been such a great day that I kind of hate to end it. How about going to the Burger 'n' Brew for dinner and then going to a movie?"

"Great!" Darcy almost said, then remembered Scott was coming over. She rolled onto her side, away from Carl, and picked up her mug. "I'd really love to, but I'm afraid, well, I'm busy." Boy, did that sound phony! "I'm sorry, Carl. I'd love to go out with you tonight, but I can't."

"That's OK. It was kind of short notice, anyway." He sat up, wrapping his arms around his knees. "Anybody I know?"

Darcy fished a marshmallow out of her mug. "Well, yes, Scott called me today, and I told him I wasn't doing anything tonight, so—"

"That's OK, I understand." Carl swallowed the last of his cocoa, put on his shoes, and then stood up. The firelight flickered on his face and made his blond hair seem even more golden. Looking up at him, Darcy caught her breath. He was so handsome. And he was really nice. Suddenly she wished with all her heart, or at least with most of it, that she hadn't told Scott he could come over that night. She could tell Carl was hurt.

She scrambled awkwardly to her feet. "Carl, I had a wonderful time today," she said softly, standing just inches away from him. She lifted her face to his. If only she could say something to make him look like the cheerful, friendly person she knew and—loved. *Do I love Carl?* she wondered. *I haven't known him long, but already he's become very special to me. Is it really love?* The thought shook her so much that she couldn't meet his eyes. If she loved Carl, then how did she feel about Scott? And if she loved Scott, as she'd taken for granted all this time, how did she really feel about Carl? You couldn't love two pepole at the same time—could you?

Carl reached out a hand and rested it lightly on her shoulder. "So did I." He was smiling again. "Practice Monday after school, right?"

"Right." Would he kiss her? She hoped he would.

And he did, very lightly and gently, on her forehead. Darcy felt disappointed.

"See you Monday," Carl said and scooped up his jacket from the chair where he'd flung it earlier. Darcy followed him to the door, wishing he wouldn't go just yet.

"I have a new original I've been working on. I'd like us to try it out," she ventured. "It's called 'A Love Like Theirs.' "

"Any good drum solos?" asked Carl.

"Probably not. It's a ballad, about a girl who wants the kind of love Heathcliff and Cathy have in *Wuthering Heights*. It's sad and dreamy, a very quiet song. Did you ever read *Wuthering Heights*? It's a great book."

"Yeah, I read it last year in English." He concentrated on zipping his jacket. "You're pretty big on love songs, aren't you?"

"Well, I guess so. Maybe because I under-stand how people feel when they're crazy in love with each other. Or I think I do." She felt herself blushing.

"I think I do, too," Carl said softly. Their eyes met and held then, and Darcy felt her knees weaken. If only he'd put his arms around her, maybe she'd know how she really felt. She was so mixed up! *Why can't things be simple?* she wondered, watching as Carl wound his striped scarf around his neck. Apparently he wasn't going to put his arms around her after all. Darcy sighed.

"See you," she said.

"See you," Carl repeated. Then he opened the front door and started down the steps.

"Watch your step!" Darcy called after him, remembering the previous night.

He grinned at her over his shoulder. "Hey, you're the one who fell down three times today!" he shouted.

"Twice!" she shouted back, laughing.

"Three times!"

"Twice!"

They kept yelling back and forth until he was too far down the street for either to hear the other's voice.

"Twice!" Darcy said smugly to herself as she closed the door.

* * *

Scott arrived around seven-thirty that night, the Jupiter tape in the pocket of his leather jacket. He and Darcy went down to the basement, and he immediately slipped the tape into the slot of Darcy's tape deck. "Wait till you hear this!" he announced.

He sat on the edge of the sofa, elbows on his knees, his entire attention on the music. He hadn't even removed his jacket. Darcy had to admit it was good—very good. It was certainly a different sound than it had been when Darcy played with them. It was harder, more raucous. Some of the songs were new, but even the originals Scott and Tommy had written when she was in the band didn't sound the same.

As she listened, Darcy was certainly impressed, just as Scott had meant her to be, but something played at the back of her mind, a thought that she tried to suppress. They were good, all right, but they weren't *distinctive*. Nothing set Jupiter apart from any other group.

What's wrong with me? Darcy asked herself. *Am I jealous? If I'd been playing*

130

with the band, would I think differently?
She couldn't answer her questions.

When the tape was over, Scott turned to her, his face alight. "So what do you think? Isn't it terrific? Jupiter's been working really hard, and now we're going to have our chance to make it!"

His enthusiasm was contagious, and Darcy firmly banished her doubts, for the time being, at least. "It's fantastic!" she agreed, knowing that was what he wanted to hear.

"Thanks," he said, touching her cheek and turning her face to his.

The old familiar magic began to take over, and Darcy felt herself drowning in his deep, dark eyes.

"Darce, I'm really sorry it didn't work out with you and Jupiter. I'd have liked you to be a part of this. You have a lot of talent."

His lips brushed hers, and Darcy thought, for at least the thousandth time, that she just didn't have any willpower where Scott was concerned.

"It'll mean a lot to Jupiter if we win the Battle of the Bands," Scott continued when they finally drew apart.

Darcy nodded, speechless, still under the spell of his kiss.

"And we *will* win, too, whether Vixen enters or not," he added, fondling a strand of her hair.

Darcy stood up abruptly, "How about a Coke?" she suggested. "I don't know about you, but I'm dying of thirst." She wasn't really, but it was the only thing she could think of to change the subject.

"Great. Thanks. And when you come back down, we'll listen to your Vixen tape. I might be able to give you a few pointers."

It was a little after ten when Scott left. But before he went, he kissed her again. No doubt about it, Scott was a great kisser. He was great at everything—well, maybe not *everything*. He'd once told Darcy casually that he might not graduate that year because his grades had fallen off and he'd been cutting class a lot. But that didn't matter, he'd added, because he didn't need a high-school diploma to make it in the music world. Darcy had wanted to ask what he'd do if he *didn't* make it, but she decided against it. She had complete faith in Scott, and she wanted to see him succeed.

Which brought her back to the Battle of the Bands. If she entered Vixen and Vixen won, which was unlikely but possible, Scott had made it plain it would ruin Jupiter's image. Where did her loyalties lie? With Scott or with Vixen?

"You look kind of down in the mouth, honey," her mother said when Darcy passed through the living room on her way to bed. "What's wrong?"

"I don't know why you keep seeing that boy," her father put in before she could answer. "He doesn't seem to make you very happy."

"Everything's fine. I'm just tired, I guess." Darcy smiled brightly. "I'm going to bed now. See you in the morning."

Darcy had a hard time falling asleep that night, in spite of the long, warm bath she'd taken to ease her muscles. She kept thinking about Jupiter and Vixen, Scott and Carl. Would she be ruining Scott's chances for a record contract if Vixen entered and won? Would she be letting Vixen down if she *didn't* enter? Would Scott be angry if she entered? Would Carl be angry if she didn't?

It was past midnight when she finally closed her eyes. She'd made her decision: first thing the next day she'd enter Vixen in the Battle of the Bands.

Chapter Ten

But in the morning Darcy had second thoughts. She'd made a decision, but she hadn't really made a choice as far as Scott and Carl were concerned. Not that either of them was pressuring her. It was just that in her own head and more important, in her heart, she felt torn between the two boys and wanted to make some kind of decision. She couldn't go on seeing both of them seriously.

What if Scott got mad at her for not taking his advice? She couldn't bear to think about that. And yet, Darcy couldn't believe he'd turn their professional competition into a personal one. She hoped he was bigger than that.

In spite of all her doubts, Darcy was convinced that, as far as Vixen was concerned, she was doing the right thing. Her first loyalty was to her band, and that's all there was to it.

So that morning in school, she tracked down Jim Steele, the senior in charge of organizing Kennedy High's Battle of the Bands, and gave him the news.

"That's great, Darcy," he said enthusiastically. "I was at the Community House Saturday night, and I thought you guys were terrific! If you hadn't entered, I was going to enter you myself. By the way, it's going to be a tough competition this year. We've got Jupiter, of course, and Hit and Run, Risk, Sin City, and now Vixen. It'll be dynamite! Ought to make a lot of money for student council."

"I hope so," said Darcy. "What's the prize this year? Not that we expect to win it, but I'm curious."

"Hey, we're going for big money this time!" Jim laughed. "Would you believe seventy-five dollars? That's twenty-five more than last year, but you already know that, since Jupiter won it last year. We figure we have to keep pace with inflation. Well, see you around, Darcy, and good luck."

"Thanks." Darcy hurried down the hall. She had English next—they were going to discuss *Wuthering Heights*—and then she was meeting Miranda in the cafeteria for lunch, when she'd tell her that she'd finally done it. Miranda would be proud of her, she knew. But what would Scott's reaction be? She supposed she'd find out soon enough.

That afternoon just before practice began, Darcy made her announcement to the rest of the group.

"All right!" cried Lori.

"Wonderful!" Beth added.

"I told you we were ready," Carl said, grinning. "But we're going to have to work extra hard from now on. Those other bands are going to be tough to beat."

"Oh, no!" Beth groaned. "You're beginning to sound just like Darcy! I've been playing so much my calluses are getting calluses!"

"Bass players are supposed to have calluses," Darcy told her cheerfully. Surrounded by her group, she felt much better about everything. "Carl's right, though. We're going to have to work as hard as we can from now on. And we have a performance coming up this weekend, so we'd better get moving."

They rehearsed for several hours and began work on "A Love Like Theirs." Until she'd actually heard Vixen play the song, Darcy hadn't been sure whether she'd do the vocal herself or give it to Beth. She decided on Beth because her voice was perfect for the wailing, soulful tune. As rocky as it was the first few times through, Darcy felt a growing excitement about the song. Each band in the battle would be expected to do at least two originals in addition to popular numbers, and she was sure they'd have the new song whipped into shape in time. So they'd do that and "Lovesick Girl." *Her* band would be playing *her* songs.

Carl stayed after the others had left. He put his arm around Darcy and gave her a warm hug. "I'm glad you went ahead with it, the Battle of the Bands, I mean," he told her. "I guess it wasn't an easy decision to make. I think I have a pretty good idea of how you feel about Scott. I mean, you've known him a long time, and you're—you're pretty tight with him, aren't you?" he asked seriously.

Darcy felt herself blushing. "Kind of, I guess. But I came to the conclusion that I had to make up my mind once and for all about what was more important—Scott or Vixen. And I decided it was Vixen."

Carl squeezed her shoulders tightly. "Hey, have you thought about how you're going to spend a quarter of seventy-five dollars when we win?" he asked teasingly.

"Not a quarter, it has to be a fifth. Miranda's working as hard as the rest of us. We can't leave her out. Let's see, one fifth of seventy-five—"

"That comes to exactly fifteen whole dollars!" shouted Carl. "With my share I'll take you out to dinner and the movies if you promise not to eat too much."

Darcy laughed. "You're on. But first we have to win it!"

At that moment it didn't seem impossible.

Darcy kept looking for Scott in the halls at school. Sometimes she saw him from a distance, but he didn't see her. Or if he did, he pretended not to.

"I think he's really mad at me, Miranda,"

she said as they walked home one afternoon. "He hasn't called or anything."

"If he's that shallow, I don't see why you *care* if he calls!" snapped Miranda. "Honestly, Darcy, a really special guy likes you a lot, and you like him, and you're still thinking about Scott Maguire. If you ask me, you're crazy!"

"Well, I *didn't* ask you, OK?" Darcy shot back. "I can't explain it, even to myself, so how can I possibly explain it to anyone else? I think maybe something's wrong with me. It can't be normal to be in love with two guys at once."

Miranda shrugged. "Who's to say what's normal? Not me, I've never been in love before."

"*Before?* You mean you're in love now?" Darcy asked eagerly. "With Billy? Boy, that was fast!"

"Come on," Miranda begged. She was blushing, and Miranda never blushed. "I think I'm in love. And I think he feels the same way about me, even though I can hardly believe it. Do you know he's called me every single night? And you know he's been picking me up after practice—and he even makes the rounds with me when I'm trying to line up gigs. Tonight he's coming over so we can study for our history exam."

Darcy listened happily to Miranda, but she couldn't help wishing her own love life were as uncomplicated as Miranda's. But she'd just have to put personal problems aside and concentrate on Vixen. And with all the performances and rehearsals coming up, that wouldn't be too hard.

Vixen's first paid engagement, Jody West's Sweet Sixteen party, went off without a hitch. Jody's parents had rented the ballroom at the Fairfield Hotel for the occasion, and it seemed to Darcy that every junior at Kennedy had been invited.

"Will you look at all those pink balloons!" Beth said, marveling. "And all that food! Mr. and Mrs. West must have spent a fortune."

"*I* think it's gaudy," pronounced Miranda. "I can't imagine anyone making such a big deal about somebody's sixteenth birthday. It's like some kind of tribal rite. When I turned sixteen, I had a few friends over, and Mom ordered an ice-cream cake from Carvel. Remember?"

Darcy nodded. "We had a great time. Did you have a Sweet Sixteen, Lori?"

"No way!" Lori said firmly. "My folks wanted to do the whole bit, but I told them I'd rather have them spend the money on a new guitar. That's how I got my Strat," she added, stroking the instrument.

"Well, I thought about it, but we couldn't afford it, so I didn't have a Sweet Sixteen, either," said Beth. She sounded a little wistful, though.

"Neither did I," Carl put in, "so I guess that makes it unanimous!"

Everybody laughed, and then Miranda said thoughtfully, "When you think about all the fifteen-year-old girls at Kennedy, I bet Vixen could keep busy the entire year just playing for Sweet Sixteens. We'd make a fortune!"

"Gimme a break," Billy said, groaning. "How many acres of pink balloons can you stand?"

Darcy laughed, "Come on, guys, let's tune up. It's time we got to work!" Darcy didn't feel the least bit nervous, only excited and eager to start playing.

When the party had finally ended and the

members of the band were packing up their instruments, Mr. West came over to Darcy and presented her with a check. "Great job," he said. "A little loud for my taste, but then I'm one of the older generation. Anyway, thanks, all of you!"

When he'd left, everyone crowded around Darcy to stare at the check. "One hundred dollars," whispered Beth. "Vixen's very first check! Darcy, you ought to frame it!"

"Frame it, my foot!" Miranda said. "Cash it!"

"How?" asked Carl.

"What do you mean, 'how'?" Darcy glanced at him, puzzled.

"Does Vixen have a bank account? The check's made out to the band," he pointed out.

"Oh, no!" wailed Miranda. "I never thought of that! Mr. West! Mr. West, we have a little problem. . . ." She dashed after him, waving the check that she'd snatched from Darcy's hand. A few minutes later she returned, all smiles. "Here we go. A brand-new check, made out to me." Then she paused and grinned impishly. "See you in a couple of weeks. I think I'll use this toward a trip to Bermuda!"

"Not without me!" added Billy, leering at her.

The laughing and kidding continued as the members of Vixen lugged all their equipment out to Carl's van. As Darcy slid into the front seat beside him, she felt a warm glow of happiness. There was something so wonderful about doing what she loved with people she liked, and then getting paid for it as well!

Carl looked over at her as he started the engine. "What are you smiling about?" he asked affectionately.

"Oh, I was just thinking that all this is so much fun, I'd almost be willing to pay people for letting us perform."

"Hold on there, boss," said Carl. "What kind of a businesswoman are you, anyway?"

Darcy laughed. "I never said I was a businesswoman. I leave all that stuff to Miranda. All I want to do is make music with my friends." Then impulsively but carefully, so as not to affect his steering, Darcy slipped her arm through Carl's and rested her head on his shoulder. Right then there was nowhere she would rather be, and no one she would rather be with.

*　　*　　*

Darcy was hurrying to school one morning in late March when she saw a familiar figure ahead of her. It was Pete Esposito, shambling along, head down, looking as though he'd lost his best friend. She caught up with him and fell into step beside him.

"Hey, Pete," she said, thinking it was a long time since she'd seen any of the members of Jupiter.

"Hi, Darcy, how's it going?" Pete replied gloomily.

"Everything's fine with me, but you don't look so hot. What's up?" she asked.

"Nothing. Everything's down. Didn't Scott tell you?"

Puzzled, Darcy said, "No, I haven't seen him lately. What are you talking about?"

"Jupiter's finished—or it will be next week."

"You're kidding!" Darcy gasped. "You're putting me on, right?"

"I'm serious. As of next Wednesday, there'll be no more Jupiter. Tommy's family's moving to Florida."

"Oh, no!" cried Darcy. "How come? Why? How long have you known?"

"Well, the plant where Tommy's dad works

laid him off over a month ago, and he's been looking for a job ever since. Finally, Tommy's uncle in Fort Lauderdale said there was an opening at the plant where he works, so they've put their house on the market, and they're leaving on Wednesday. This just happened last week."

"I can't believe it! You must all be wrecked. How's Scott taking it?"

Pete shrugged. "He's pretty bummed out. He tried everything to get Tommy to stay, even told him he could move in with his folks; and Tommy would have, too, but his parents said no way. So he's going, and Jupiter doesn't have a drummer."

"But you've been auditioning, haven't you? There must be dozens of drummers around."

"Sure there are, but none of them is as good as Tommy. I'm really surprised you hadn't heard about this. I thought everybody knew."

Darcy sighed. "I've been so busy, I haven't heard anything at all, and neither has the rest of the my band." She felt terrible. Poor Scott! No wonder he hadn't called lately and had seemed to avoid her in the halls. He'd had such high hopes for a record contract, but it couldn't happen now unless he found another drummer as good as Tommy.

"Scott's not really thinking of breaking up the band, is he? I mean, eventually you'll get another good drummer. I know it."

Pete didn't seem to be convinced, but he gave a faint smile. "Sure. Sure we will. But whoever we end up with, we won't be able to whip him into shape for the Battle of the Bands. That's only a week and a half away. Oh, well, so much for Jupiter's winning again."

They had reached the school now, and Pete raised a hand in farewell. "See ya, Darcy." He plodded up the steps, leaving Darcy staring after him, a lump in her throat. Tears stung her eyes. She'd wanted so much for Vixen to win the competition, but not this way. Even if Jupiter played, it wouldn't be a fair fight, and if Vixen won, some of the triumph would be taken out of it.

But that wasn't what was making her so miserable. It was the thought of how Scott must be feeling, how disappointed and angry and frustrated he must be.

Darcy brushed the tears from her eyes

and ran up the steps. If Scott were in school, she'd find him. She had to talk to him. Not that there was much of anything she could do to help, but at least she could be there if he needed her.

She was concentrating so hard on searching for Scott that she didn't notice Carl beside her until he waved a hand in front of her face, saying, "Hey, wake up! It's me, Carl." Then he took a closer look and said, "Darcy? You OK? You look like you've been crying."

"I have, kind of," she admitted. "I just heard the news about Jupiter."

"What news? Somebody get hurt or something?"

"No, nothing like that." Darcy proceeded to tell him what Pete had told her.

"I guess I understand, kind of," Carl said when she was finished. "It's a real tough break. But they'll land on their feet. You can't keep a good band down," he added, joking, but Darcy didn't smile.

Just then the bell rang for first period. Darcy told Carl she'd see him at practice that afternoon and joined the crowd moving down the hall. She was going to have a hard time keeping her mind on schoolwork that day.

Darcy didn't catch sight of Scott until classes were over that afternoon. He was on his way out the main doors, and Darcy ran after him, calling his name. He turned, and when he saw her, he gave his usual lopsided grin.

"Hi, Darcy. Where've you been keeping yourself?" he asked.

"I've been pretty busy," she said breathlessly, then plunged ahead. "I talked to Pete today. He told me Tommy's leaving."

"Yeah, bad, huh?" But Scott didn't seem upset at all. "Well, drummers are a dime a dozen," he continued. "We'll probably pick up somebody in the next couple of days. No sweat."

Darcy felt deflated. Here she was offering sympathy and support, but Scott didn't seem to want either.

"I—I just wanted to tell you how sorry I am," she said, faltering. "Not just because of Jupiter, but because Tommy's your best friend, and all. I know if Miranda moved away, I'd be pretty upset."

Scott shrugged. "That's the breaks. Who knows? Maybe they'll move back to town if his dad's job doesn't work out. Listen, Darce, it's been great talking to you, but I've got to get moving. We have a lot of drummers to audition this afternoon."

"Yeah, sure . . ." said Darcy.

She watched him bound down the steps, greet some girls who were passing by, and join a couple of boys who had been waiting for him impatiently. He didn't look back.

He just doesn't want me to see how he really feels, Darcy told herself. *I was crazy to think he'd open up to me. He's too proud, too sensitive.* But cutting through her own thoughts, she could hear Miranda saying, "It's about time you realized that the only thing Scott cares about is Scott."

"Oh, shut up, Miranda!" she said to the voice.

But for the second time that day, she found herself blinking back the tears.

Chapter Eleven

Vixen was gathered in Darcy's basement on the Saturday before the Battle of the Bands. They were about to launch into "Heartbreaker" when Billy came pounding down the stairs.

"Have I got news for you!" he shouted. "Check this out! Jupiter has a new drummer—they signed him up last week—and Hit and Run has dropped out of the Battle! Jupiter's definitely going to play, and a lot of people are pretty mad."

"Wow," said Darcy. "It's too bad about Hit and Run, but it's great that Jupiter's back in business. Why should that make anybody mad?"

"Yeah, why?" echoed Lori.

"Because," said Billy, flopping down on the sofa beside Miranda, "the reason Hit and Run dropped out is that their drummer, Jeff, went over to Jupiter! Just left them flat. Now the Hit and Run guys are burned at Jupiter, and all their fans are threatening to boycott the contest."

"No kidding!" Darcy gasped. "I can't believe Jeff Michaels would pull something like that!"

"And I can't believe Scott would take him on. He must've known he'd be asking for trouble. It's kind of like—like sabotage!" said Beth.

"He knew Hit and Run wouldn't be able to compete without Jeff. Next to Tommy, he's one of the best drummers around—present company excepted," Lori added, with a glance at Carl. Carl said nothing, just sat behind his drums, his face expressionless.

"I'm not all that surprised," Miranda said quietly. "Everybody knows there's nothing Scott wouldn't do to help Jupiter succeed."

Darcy was more shaken than she let herself show. She didn't know Jeff Michaels very well, but he'd often come to watch rehearsals when she was in Jupiter. And once or twice

Tommy had let him sit in on drums while he took a break. But she just couldn't imagine anybody walking out on his own band, especially not at a time like this.

Suddenly a thought struck her. Had Scott already lined up Jeff when she'd spoken to him the week before? Was that the reason he'd seemed to take Tommy's leaving so lightly? She didn't want to think about it.

"Look, gang," she said, hoping her voice sounded firm and confident, "this really isn't any of our business. It's between Jupiter and Hit and Run. What we have to do is get *our* act together. Come on, let's practice."

Once again the band began to play, but Darcy was uncomfortably aware of Miranda and Billy whispering together as the music blasted out of the amps. Carl seemed preoccupied and fouled up a couple of drum cues, which wasn't like him. Everybody seemed to be a little off that afternoon, including Darcy.

It isn't any of our business, she told herself. *It has absolutely nothing to do with Vixen.* But somehow she had a feeling that it did.

An hour later, Darcy called a halt to the rehearsal. It was pointless to go on since they didn't have their minds on the music. As usual Carl stayed after the others had left, but he looked as glum as she felt.

Darcy sat at her keyboard, too upset to be still. "He was only thinking of Jupiter," she said angrily. "It wasn't as though he went out and kidnapped Jeff! If anyone's to blame, it's Jeff Michaels. He had no right to leave Hit and Run without any warning."

Carl came over to her and rested a hand on her shoulder. "Darcy, there's something I think I'd better tell you—" he began, but Darcy shrugged off his hand.

"I don't want to hear it! I'm sick and tired of everybody bad-mouthing Scott! Just leave me alone, OK?"

Carl stood beside her for a moment, then turned away. "Whatever you say. But as you said yourself, this is between Jupiter and Hit and Run. So don't let it get to you. Scott can take care of himself. He doesn't need you to stand up for him. Don't let him tie you up in knots this way."

"You're just jealous!" Darcy flared up and was immediately sorry.

Carl nodded, the ghost of a smile on his lips. "You bet I am! I love you, Darcy, and I hoped you were beginning to feel the same way about me. But whenever things are going well with us, Scott comes between us. Sure, I'm jealous. I want you to be my girlfriend, but you can't make up your mind between Scott or me. And I want you all to myself." He leaned over and kissed her gently.

Darcy clung to him, so torn by conflicting emotions that she couldn't think straight. "I love you, too, Carl," she whispered, knowing it was true. "But—"

"There's always a 'but,' " Carl said and gave a rueful laugh. He held her at arm's length, looking deep into her eyes.

"I'm so mixed up! Don't give up on me, please," she pleaded.

"Just don't *you* give up on *me*."

Carl kissed her again, this time on the tip of her nose. A few minutes later, he was gone, leaving Darcy standing alone in the middle of the room, more confused than she'd been in her whole life.

The members of Vixen stood huddled together just offstage in the Kennedy auditorium, craning their necks to watch Sin City perform their final number. Darcy couldn't believe it. The Battle of the Bands was now. Vixen's big day had arrived. Darcy and her group had walked onstage and put on one of their best shows ever. Now Chris Dimon, lead guitarist and vocalist of Sin City, was leaping all over the stage, screaming unintelligible lyrics into the mike.

"Old Chris is really going all out," Lori whispered in Darcy's ear. "Maybe he'll blow his amp out!"

Darcy shook her head. "No such luck. They've got top-notch equipment. And they're good, a lot better than I thought they'd be."

"Not better than Vixen," Carl said. "Different style, a lot of energy, but musically they're pretty ragged."

Darcy looked across to the opposite wing. In the shadows she could see Scott, Pete, Charlie, and in the background, Jeff Michaels. They were checking out the competition, too. Jupiter had been the second band to perform, after Risk, and Vixen had followed them. It was always the last band that stuck in the audience's mind.

She wondered what Scott was thinking right then. Jupiter had sounded surprisingly good, considering the short time they'd had to rehearse with their new drummer. When they'd come out onstage, they'd been greeted with cheers and screams from the hard-core Jupiter groupies, mingled with boos and cat-calls from a few Hit and Run fans. But once they'd started to play, they held the audience in the palms of their hands.

Even without Hit and Run, the competition was fierce. All Darcy's personal problems seemed small compared to her desire to win. Vixen deserved it. They'd worked so hard!

Cheers and applause filled the auditorium as Sin City finished their number. Darcy clutched Carl's hand, squeezing it so tightly he winced. In just a few minutes, the winner would be announced. Darcy felt weak-kneed. Vixen had worked so hard and performed so well. Would it be enough? And if Vixen won, how would Scott feel toward Darcy?

Jim Steele ran onstage and called out the name of each band. To Darcy's ears, the audience reaction to each name seemed the same. How could anybody possibly tell who had won?

"I can't stand it!" screamed Beth, jumping up and down.

"Cool it," Carl whispered, pressing a firm

hand on her shoulder. "Jim's about to make the announcement."

Darcy clasped Carl's other hand and held her breath.

"And the winner is—*Vixen!*" Jim announced.

It seemed as though the roof would be blasted off as the audience applauded, yelled, whistled, and stamped their feet. Dazed, Darcy felt herself being pulled onto the stage. She had a momentary glimpse of Miranda and Billy hugging each other ecstatically in the wings; then she, Carl, Lori, and Beth were taking their bows, grinning, and waving at the crowd.

We did it! We did it! she repeated to herself over and over. *Vixen's number one!*

Jim thrust an envelope into Darcy's hand and shouted, "Congratulations!"

The members of the other bands came out then, to mounting applause and cheers. If she'd been excited when Jupiter had won, Darcy was a hundred times more thrilled now.

Darcy never quite knew how she got offstage, except she was aware of Carl's hand on her arm, guiding her through the crowd. Then they all were hugging and kissing one another, and laughing and shouting. The entire backstage area was jammed with kids, and each one of them seemed to want to congratulate every member of Vixen. By the time the crowd began to thin out, Darcy was more than ready for a little peace and quiet. She looked around for Carl and found him with Billy, packing up the instruments and amps. She was on her way to join them when she ran smack into Scott.

"Hey, slow down!" he said, laughing. "What's your hurry? Now that you're a big star, don't you have time for your old pals?"

"Oh, Scott!" she cried. "I didn't see you, honest." Was Carl watching? she wondered. She glanced around and saw Carl heading out the back door carrying an amp.

"Seriously, Darcy," Scott continued, draping an arm around her shoulders, "Vixen was terrific. This is the first time I've seen you perform since the Community House. You've turned into real pros, no joke."

"Thanks," Darcy whispered. "Jupiter sounded great, too."

"Not as good as we did with Tommy, but that's the breaks. Jeff's OK. He'll shape up after a while. You remember how he always used to hang around when we had practice? He's been bugging me for years to let him into Jupiter, so when he showed up for our auditions, I figured why not? I mean, it's too bad about Hit and Run, but it was his decision." He turned her around to face him. "Do you have a few minutes? I want to talk to you about something."

"Sure. I guess so," said Darcy, though she felt guilty about not helping the others break down their equipment. "What is it?"

Scott led her to a big, dusty mound of folded stage curtains and pulled her down beside him. "About your future," he said solemnly.

"My future?" Darcy repeated stupidly. "What future?"

"Your future as a musician. I'm going to say something to you that I hardly ever say. I made a mistake, a big mistake, when I replaced you with Charlie. Not that he's not good—he is. But I was wrong when I thought Jupiter didn't need a keyboardist. Watching you up there tonight, I realized how talented you really are. I've got to admit it—your originals are better than ours." He paused and looked down at his feet. Darcy sat silently, unable to believe her ears. It was almost exactly the way she'd dreamed it a few months ago. Scott had said he was wrong! *Then why doesn't it make me feel good?* she asked herself. Instead, she felt very uncomfortable.

"Thanks," she said again, wondering what was coming next and afraid she knew.

"What I'm really saying is, how about coming back to Jupiter? You made your point. You proved you could make it on your own. I want you back, Darcy. What about it?"

"I—" Darcy fumbled, at a loss for words. This was what she'd longed to hear—once. But now everything was different. Vixen wasn't just a lot of ideas scribbled down on sheets of paper. It was people, real people—all of whom had as big a stake in Vixen's success as she did. Now that her dream had come true, could she just turn her back on her friends? And how could Scott expect her to?

"Scott, I can't. I just can't," she told him quietly.

He stared at her, incredulous. "What do you mean, you can't? This is the big time, Darcy. We'll cut another tape. You'll write some new originals. You'll even do lead vocals. We'll get that record contract, no question. I'm not talking kid stuff, Battle of the Bands at Kennedy High and gigs in the basements of churches. I'm talking about the professional music scene—recordings and tours and more money than you've ever seen in your life!" He took her hands in his and leaned closer to her. "I'm also talking about you and me. I guess you know by now how I feel about you. You're the only girl I've ever cared about."

"Are you saying you're in love with me?" Darcy asked.

Scott hesitated and looked away. "Sure, I'm in love with you. If I weren't in love with you, would I be pleading with you like this?"

Darcy stood up, gently pulling her hands away from his. "I think maybe you would," she said quietly. "I think you'd say just about anything if it would help Jupiter get to the top. But that's not the point. The point is, I can't leave Vixen. It's my band; they're my friends. I can't just walk away from them like they didn't matter, the way Jeff did with Hit and Run. Not for all the money and fame in the world. Not even to be your girlfriend." She took a deep breath. "Just tell me one thing, Scott. Will you still want me to be your girl if I stick with Vixen? Or is it a package deal?"

Scott stood up, too, scowling now. "What kind of a guy do you think I am, anyway?"

Darcy looked up at him, shaking her head. "I thought I knew. I thought I understood you. But I was wrong. I guess we were both wrong, about a lot of things."

She could see Carl standing by the back door, leaning against the wall, deliberately not looking in her direction.

"I have to go, Scott. Vixen has some celebrating to do."

As she walked away, she heard him call her, "I'll talk to you tomorrow, OK?"

Darcy didn't answer. She went up to Carl and slipped her arm through his. "Where are the rest of the kids? I have a great idea—let's blow the whole prize money on a party to end all parties! We can go to the all-night deli and pick up soda and food, then go back to my house. What do you say?"

Carl's face was grave. "OK by me. I just have one question: who am I going to the party with, my girlfriend or Scott's?"

Darcy beamed at him. "That's the dumbest question I ever heard!" She stood on tiptoe and kissed him on the mouth. "*Your* girlfriend is starving to death. Let's get a move on!"

Several hours later, after Vixen and their friends had consumed dozens of sandwiches and drunk gallons of soda, Darcy sat snuggled up next to Carl on the sofa in the Bennetts' basement. Most of the crowd had left, and those who remained were listening to music and talking quietly. Miranda and Billy were curled up together in an armchair, holding hands and looking sleepy.

After a long silence, Carl tipped Darcy's chin up with one finger and asked, "You've really gotten Scott out of your system?"

Darcy nodded, tightening her arms around him. "Once and for all. I'm just sorry it took so long. I guess I'm not very quick on the uptake. But I'd thought I was in love with Scott so long it had become a habit, you know? Like biting your fingernails, or something."

Darcy could feel Carl's laugh before she heard it. "I understand. If you're sure you're cured, I'll tell you what I was going to say last week. You remember, when I finally broke down and told you how I felt about you?"

"Yes, I dimly recall." Darcy giggled. But she saw that Carl was completely serious. "What is it?"

"Jeff didn't audition for Jupiter on his own. Scott *asked* him to try out. I know because he asked me, too, and when I said there was no way I'd walk out on Vixen, he told me it wasn't a big deal, Jeff Michaels would do it. Scott broke up Hit and Run, not Jeff. And if he could have, he'd have broken up Vixen, too. I decided not to tell you because I thought you wouldn't believe me. I was afraid you'd think I was putting Scott down so I could make points with you. And I didn't want that to happen. You had to make up your own mind."

Darcy wasn't surprised or shocked. It was as though she'd known all along.

"I'm glad you waited till now to tell me. And more than anything, I'm glad you still want me to be your girlfriend, even though I've been acting like a perfect idiot."

Carl grinned at her, blue eyes twinkling. "Nobody's perfect," he said, and then he kissed her softly.

We hope you enjoyed reading this book. All the titles currently available in the Sweet Dreams series are listed on the next two pages. They are all available at your local bookshop or newsagent, though should you find any difficulty in obtaining the books you would like, you can order direct from the publisher, at the address below. Also, if you would like to know more about the series, or would simply like to tell us what you think of the series, write to:

Kim Prior,
Sweet Dreams,
Transworld Publishers Limited,
Century House,
61–63 Uxbridge Road,
London W5 5SA.

or
Kiri Martin
c/o Corgi & Bantam Books New Zealand,
9 Waipareira Avenue,
Henderson,
Auckland,
New Zealand.

To order books, please list the title(s) you would like, and send together with your name and address, and a cheque or postal order made payable to TRANSWORLD PUBLISHERS LIMITED. Please allow cost of book(s) plus 20p for the first book and 10p for each additional book for postage and packing.

Sweet Dreams®

20323	1	**P.S. I LOVE YOU (1)**	*Barbara Conklin*	£1.25
20325	8	**THE POPULARITY PLAN (2)**	*Rosemary Vernon*	£1.25
20327	4	**LAURIE'S SONG (3)**	*Suzanne Rand*	£1.25
20328	2	**PRINCESS AMY (4)**	*Melinda Pollowitz*	£1.10
20326	6	**LITTLE SISTER (5)**	*Yvonne Greene*	£1.10
20324	X	**CALIFORNIA GIRL (6)**	*Janet Quin-Harkin*	£1.25
20604	4	**GREEN EYES (7)**	*Suzanne Rand*	£1.25
20601	X	**THE THOROUGHBRED (8)**	*Joanna Campbell*	65p
20744	X	**COVER GIRL (9)**	*Yvonne Greene*	£1.25
20745	8	**LOVE MATCH (10)**	*Janet Quin-Harkin*	£1.25
20787	3	**THE PROBLEM WITH LOVE (11)**	*Rosemary Vernon*	£1.25
20788	1	**NIGHT OF THE PROM (12)**	*Debra Spector*	£1.25
17779	6	**THE SUMMER JENNY FELL IN LOVE (13)**	*Barbara Conklin*	£1.10
17780	X	**DANCE OF LOVE (14)**	*Jocelyn Saal*	£1.10
17781	8	**THINKING OF YOU (15)**	*Jeanette Nobile*	£1.10
17782	6	**HOW DO YOU SAY GOODBYE? (16)**	*Margaret Burman*	75p
17783	4	**ASK ANNIE (17)**	*Suzanne Rand*	£1.25
17784	2	**TEN BOY SUMMER (18)**	*Janet Quin-Harkin*	75p
17791	5	**LOVE SONG (19)**	*Anne Park*	75p
17792	3	**THE POPULARITY SUMMER (20)**	*Rosemary Vernon*	£1.25
17793	1	**ALL'S FAIR IN LOVE (21)**	*Jeanne Andrews*	£1.10
17794	X	**SECRET IDENTITY (22)**	*Joanna Campbell*	£1.25
17797	4	**FALLING IN LOVE AGAIN (23)**	*Barbara Conklin*	£1.25
17800	8	**THE TROUBLE WITH CHARLIE (24)**	*Jay Ellen*	£1.25
17795	8	**HER SECRET SELF (25)**	*Rhondi Vilott*	£1.10
17796	6	**IT MUST BE MAGIC (26)**	*Marian Woodruff*	£1.10
17798	2	**TOO YOUNG FOR LOVE (27)**	*Gailanne Maravel*	£1.10
17801	6	**TRUSTING HEARTS (28)**	*Jocelyn Saal*	£1.25
17813	X	**NEVER LOVE A COWBOY (29)**	*Jesse Dukore*	95p
17814	8	**LITTLE WHITE LIES (30)**	*Lois I. Fisher*	£1.25
17839	3	**TOO CLOSE FOR COMFORT (31)**	*Debra Spector*	95p
17840	7	**DAYDREAMER (32)**	*Janet Quin-Harkin*	95p
17841	5	**DEAR AMANDA (33)**	*Rosemary Vernon*	£1.25
17842	3	**COUNTRY GIRL (34)**	*Melinda Pollowitz*	95p
17843	1	**FORBIDDEN LOVE (35)**	*Marian Woodruff*	95p
17844	X	**SUMMER DREAMS (36)**	*Barbara Conklin*	£1.25
17846	6	**PORTRAIT OF LOVE (37)**	*Jeanette Nobile*	95p
17847	4	**RUNNING MATES (38)**	*Jocelyn Saal*	£1.25
17848	2	**FIRST LOVE (39)**	*Debra Spector*	£1.25
17849	0	**SECRETS (40)**	*Anna Aaron*	85p